Fowler's Footsteps

Wildfowler with eight-bore on Cley Bank

FOWLER'S FOOTSTEPS

PHIL GRAY

with sporting wishes

Phil Gray

Illustrated by the author

Reedbush Press 2007

First published by Reedbush Press, East Northamptonshire 2007

© Phil Gray 2007

ISBN 978-0-9541994-2-5

Other books by the same author
The Washlanders
Fenland Fowler
A Fenman in Africa

**This book is dedicated to
my grandson Thomas Gray**

Printed in Great Britain by
www.printondemand-worldwide.com
Peterborough

Contents

Acknowledgements

My grateful thanks are due to the late Nigel Thornycroft who tried to encourage me to write this book twenty years ago. To the late Patrick Kearney for the jacket photograph, to all those characters that appear in the story, sometimes under their own name, more often not. Last, but by no means least, I thank Anne Canterbury and Robert Gray for their valuable contribution of time spent proof reading the manuscript.

Foreword

Before I wrote my first book *The Washlanders*, my good friend, the late Nigel Thornycroft, suggested that I put it together in the style of his own book *Fowler's Moon*, which was written as the story through the first season after a young man's introduction to wildfowling. I was reluctant to follow his advice because I felt that it would be borrowing his idea, and in any case the style would not have worked with my original content.

However, that was twenty years ago and since then I have met many people who consider *Fowler's Moon* to be the best fowling book that they have read. These same people have told me that they are hungry for a book written in similar style, so here it is. I would not claim *Fowler's Footsteps* to be in any way equal to Thornycroft's book, but if it comes close to satisfying a need expressed then I will have played my part.

Some readers will recognise themselves in this book. Others might be convinced that in certain passages they are Alec and friends. All I will say is that the shooting days described in the book happened at the time of year, during the same weather and tide conditions as stated in the text. As there is nothing new under the sun, many wildfowlers and rough shooters will have had similar experiences. The hope is that this book will trigger memories of the reader's own times on marsh and in field, to be relived as the book falls unheeded, having achieved its purpose.

Phil Gray

Oundle
East Northamptonshire
April 2007

THE WILDFOWLER'S PRAYER.

Give me, Oh Lord
    A sporting heart,
Not to disgrace
    The gunners art,
And all I ask —
    A trusty gun,
An untierd body
    When work be done;
A steady hand —
    A watchful eye
A quickened ear,
    A cloudy sky;
Ten thousand geese
    All flying low
Above the spot
    Where I shall go.
And so this night Lord
    Shall I be
At peace with man,
    Myself and Thee.

Renary J. Gerry.

1

August 18

The well-worn English joke that our summer consists of three fine days and a thunderstorm was brought to the forefront of the mind as the thunder rolled and rumbled dramatically in the distance. The atmosphere was less oppressive by far now that the storm had finally broken and the torrential rain had been welcomed in that it brought a blessed freshness to the air. Immediately after the rain the humidity had actually increased for a little while, but thankfully that had passed and now wisps of steam rose from the road where the tarmac had retained some of the heat from the past seventy-two blistering hours. I had been helping a farming cousin with his harvest, but the rain had put a temporary stop to that. As the storm slowly moved further away my thoughts turned to the pile of correspondence and other paperwork that had lain unattended for the best part of a week. Without much enthusiasm I decided I had better make a start on it. Fifteen minutes later the task was interrupted by the persistent ring of the telephone on the little table in the hall.

The caller was an old friend whom I hadn't seen for some time, enquiring as to how the world was treating me. Alec and I went back a long way through our common interest in shooting in most of its forms, particularly wildfowling. He had worked as a draughtsman for a company in Norwich in those days. The job had allowed a certain flexibility of working hours, of which Alec had taken full advantage.

We had haunted the shores of The Wash for several seasons, before he had to move away due to work commitments. Now, it transpired, he was back in Norfolk.

After we had exchanged the usual information relating to the activities and news of our respective families Alec changed the tone of the conversation saying. "Look, if you're free at the weekend why don't you come over for a drink? Bring your gun just in case we get a chance for a walk." It so happened that there was nothing planned for the weekend so it was agreed that I would turn up sometime on the Friday evening.

Alec and Molly lived in north Norfolk on the outskirts of a remote but pretty village. Their cottage was typical of the area, flint faced with a red pan-tiled roof. It stood facing a minor road, whilst to the rear there was an acre of garden beyond which the land sloped down for a mile to where a winding hedge hid the road to the coast. After the hedge the land rose gently again for another three miles to a belt of scotch pines, which formed the horizon at that point. I knew that not so very far beyond that protective barrier of high ground lay the saltings, fresh marshes and the seascapes of this picturesque corner of our land.

There was a gravelled yard at the back of the house with a garage and some outbuildings. The latter included a small chicken house for Molly's hens and a kennel with a run. Then came a large square of lawn after which was the

2

vegetable garden. Through this ran a central path to the bottom of the acre, which was rough grass dotted with a dozen apple trees and a couple of plum trees. The latter were fairly laden and promised well for next month. Among the fruit trees was a fenced area, which housed Alec's small collection of wildfowl. Like many such collections, this had all started with one bird, a wing-tipped wigeon that Alec had brought down one winters' dawn. Seeing it was only slightly injured he took it home where it soon recovered and settled down to its new life.

When I arrived on that Friday evening I drew in and parked the car in the yard to be met by Rosy, Alec's yellow labrador who came ambling across the gravel wagging her tail in greeting. Her master popped his head out of a shed door;

"Take your bags in. Molly's indoors, I'll be with you in a minute." I walked into the kitchen to find Molly dressing a potato salad.

"Hello there," she smiled. "We've put you in the spare room at the back. Go and park your things while I put the kettle on."

By the time I had planted my holdall in the little bedroom and returned to the kitchen Alec was there lounging in a high-backed carver sipping a cup of tea. Molly sat opposite him and my cup stood waiting near an empty chair.

"I was just stacking some logs in the shed," Alec said. "Some dead branches blew off one of the older apple trees last March and I've only just got round to sawing them up. At least they are well dried out now."

An hour later we sat down making short work of the salad. Molly had to attend a meeting at the village hall so Alec and I made our way into what he called his study, but I always thought it had more of the air of a den about it. Yes, there was a desk there and an ancient steel filing cabinet, but there were also a pair of comfortable looking armchairs and a small table upon which stood a bottle of Famous Grouse. In the niché between the chimney breast and the wall two stout shelves housed my friend's collection of sporting books - Duncan & Thorne's *Complete Wildfowler Ashore & Afloat* and Peter Scott's *Morning Flight* and *Wild Chorus*. "BB" and that good old Breydoner A H Patterson were well represented. W A Dutt's *Norfolk Broads* caught my eye, as I was aware of the beautiful watercolours by Frank Southgate that were liberally distributed throughout the text. Standing upon a third shelf were some of Alec's mounted birds - a pair of curlew, some redshank, a shoveler and a little group of wigeon, all in lifelike stances as though waiting for the tide to turn. Looking somewhat out of place at the end was a red grouse standing erect, for all the world as if it had posed for the picture on the label of the whisky bottle.

In the niché on the opposite side of the fireplace Alec had made a simple gun rack by fitting a shelf at waist height and another about three feet above it. The top shelf had two-inch diameter holes bored through and spaced at intervals of three inches. The small armoury consisted of a Bland boxlock ejector, a magnum also by Bland, another, older, magnum by BSA and a nice looking Greener 10-bore hammer gun. Standing together at one end were a sturdy looking sea rod and a Hardy fly rod. I had borrowed the BSA occasionally and enjoyed shooting with it, although weighing in at eight pounds it was not a gun to take for a walk through acres of sugar beet. Its proper environment is most definitely the marshland. One or two prints adorned the walls including one by Southgate, which I had always coveted, a flight of golden plover skimming over a stubble field where a covey

4

of partridges squatted among the stooks. Alec caught me gazing at it and smiled.

"You like that picture don't you?"

"Always have," I replied.

"Well," he went on, "when we have lowered the level in this bottle you will notice that the number of birds in the scene appear to increase!"

We duly got down to the task of lowering the tide of whisky, which was not an onerous task by any means. Thus engaged, we talked on as the large clock on the wall above the desk solemnly ticked away the minutes and then the hours. Rosy sprawled out on the rug before the empty fireplace, content to be wherever her master parked himself.

Alec retold the tales of his younger days highlighted by the excitement of shooting rabbits in the harvest field. This was in the days before combined harvesters when tractors towed binders that cut, bunched, tied and threw out sheaves of corn at regular intervals along the field. As the area of standing corn was gradually reduced rabbits began to make a run for it across the stubble towards the hedges. There were usually one or two guns out and the shooting could become quite wild and in some cases downright dangerous. Entertaining though the stories were, the whisky was beginning to take effect and more than once I felt myself nodding. I awoke with a start to find Alec lolling back with his mouth open. I think his sudden snore woke me and as I moved he stirred.

"Blast!" he muttered. "Good anaesthetic isn't it? I didn't mean to drop off and besides; I want a clear head by morning. We'd better turn in. See you at breakfast."

While Alec was occupied putting Rosy out for the night I stumbled my way up to my room and it wasn't long before I was oblivious to the world.

In the morning, thanks to my habit of sleeping with a window open whatever the weather, my head was reasonably clear of the fumes of the Scottish spirit and I peered out of the window to greet a fine day. Alec had obviously survived the night for he was down at the wildfowl pen feeding his birds. At breakfast Molly pulled our legs for falling asleep like a couple of old timers.

"You didn't hear me come in last night, neither of you, I thought I'd leave you to it," she laughed.

Alec ignored the chaff and buttered a slice of toast.

"There's an uncut wheat field on George's land where a storm the other week flattened about an acre, he said. "It was recovering, but then the recent storm knocked down a bit more. This field is well ripe and the pigeons have found it. They won't be able to cut it today so I thought we'd have a go at the old pigeons while we have the chance." As soon as we had finished breakfast we collected our trappings, piled them into the ample rear section of my estate car and set off for George's small farm. The farm couldn't have been above three miles away, but the narrow hedged-in roads gave the illusion that it was much further than it actually was. As we pulled into the yard we spotted George working his way around a small combined harvester with a grease gun. After he had delivered the customary grumble about the weather he said that he had seen a tidy few pigeons dropping into the wheat field about this time yesterday. We turned the car around and made our way along a dirt track to park as near to the field as we could.

As we walked into the field half a dozen pigeons clattered up from the flattened patch. From his earlier reconnaissance Alec had earmarked the likeliest place to make our hides, but that had been on a windy day - today there was not even a breeze. Refusing to be discouraged we optimistically put up

6

our poles and netting with a hedge as background. Alec set out his decoys and we settled down expecting the usual long wait. In point of fact the first birds came after only a few minutes, sweeping over the decoys presenting good shots for both guns. It seemed quite some time before the last of the grey and white feathers drifted to earth in the airless atmosphere. It was then though that the waiting really began.

At first it was pleasant to be able to sit comfortably in shirtsleeves, instead of being numbed by the icy winds of winter. Later though, as the sun climbed higher in the cloudless sky, beads of perspiration trickled down my forehead into my eyes and the hide became a suntrap of almost oven-like proportions. A good hour had passed without another pigeon showing up; in truth the only other sign of life I had seen was a company of rooks making their way over a distant spinney. Normally I would have been thinking about calling it a day by now, or at least moving elsewhere, but apart from trying for some sport the idea today was to protect George's wheat. Dutifully we hung on, slowly roasting as the flies buzzed around our heads. Our heads weren't the only place they were buzzing; I noticed that my pigeon was already flyblown and I correctly guessed that Alec's bird had received the same attention.

Only two more woodpigeons came to that field. One came high over the hedge from behind and was brought down by my friend. The other swerved off before coming into range. It was a very hot and red-faced pair of guns who stumbled back to the car and thence to report to George that his wheat appeared to be safe for today. There was nothing to be done then but to head back to the village pub to urgently replace our loss of body fluids with a couple of pints of bitter shandy. Over our drinks Alec paused between swallows to say.

"Look, don't let us lose touch. Even though this morning wasn't great, it reminded me of some good outings we have had, so let's make a point of sharing a few days together this season. What do you think?" It so happened that I had been thinking along similar lines while I scanned the horizon from the hide, so there was only one possible reply. The upshot was that I was invited to come and stay again next month for an early walk after partridges. It was with that happy thought that I drove homewards to the fen country.

2

September 1

Due to the early hour of daybreak I would have enough time before work, to enjoy a morning flight on the first day of the duck-shooting season. I lost no time making plans. On the first of September, round our way at least, one is always likely to see duck even if a shot doesn't present itself, for the simple reason that there are always lots of guns out. Members of the local wildfowling club on the fresh marshes and the bank of the tidal river, guns waiting by the drains on the farms and even farm workers making an early start on the fields can put duck on the move.

On most days the fowl would merely drop into a quiet spot and lie up in relative security during the day, not bothering to move much until dusk when the urge to feed motivated them. On this day those quiet spots are far fewer, and the two or three hours when the duck are on the wing can provide the gunner with some exciting sport.

In eager anticipation of just such sport I rose very early on the day and was reminded just how early it was by a muffled murmur from beneath the sheets as I eased out of bed in the vain hope of slipping away having caused no disturbance. I did not quite catch all of the words but "middle of the something night" came through fairly clearly. Escaping swiftly down the stairs I congratulated myself for having the good sense to lay out my clothes and equipment in readiness.

Before very long I was driving across the fen through a low mist that hung like a grey curtain a few feet above the black earth. As I turned into a side road, the road sign announced its name on wooden rails all but obliterated by a thick growth of reeds from a nearby dyke; a barn owl was lit whitely in the beam of the headlights as it glided by.

By 4.20 am I had parked the car under the bank and passed through a five-barred, galvanized gate that was absolutely dripping condensation. It was so drenched that too close a contact could have resulted in an unwelcome and unnecessary early wetting. Another ten minutes and I was treading down a space in the rushes by the side of a drain on the edge of Guyhirn Wash. Young Jet, watched patiently until I was satisfied with the results of my stamping around and then joined me in the hollow as we settled down to the wildfowler's continuing pastime; the wait. As usual I was early, but why hang around if you are awake and ready to go? It is good to have time to relax with a pipe and a flask of hot coffee or tea and take in one's surroundings before the much-anticipated activity of the morning. The view did not stretch very far for the first half hour, but gradually the field of vision increased as the grey lightness in the east began to spread.

The dawn came pinkly, with tall columns of mist gliding along the surface of the water, driven by the slightest puff of a breeze. It wasn't even enough to be called a breeze; it was more of a zephyr. A heron appeared looking huge against the mist, glided like a pterodactyl over my head, braked and swung its long legs down to alight gently at the drain side no more than seventy yards from the hide. This lanky fisherman remained motionless for a moment and then, after shaking its plumage back into place, waded forward into the water and became a picture of avid concentration. I could see it clearly against the gleaming surface of the drain. It wasn't at all distracted by the first shots of the morning, though they came only as faint pops on the still air, fired by some optimistic gunner out on the washes not so very far from my position.

Soon I began to see teams of mallard on the move, but only as tiny specks flying along the washland. There appeared to be plenty of duck about, with some in view for most of the time. Certainly after one spattering of shots a pack of over a hundred whirled around, climbing rapidly to gain the height that they would quickly learn was safely out of reach of the intruders in their marshes. One or two teal could be seen among the panicking throng and when compared with the heavier mallard, because of their smaller size, they appeared to be flying much faster than they actually were. I was so intent on watching them that I almost missed my first opportunity. A flickering shape was flying towards me, keeping exactly to the line of the drain. As the gun came to the shoulder the silhouette of the duck's bill against the eastern sky identified it as a shoveler. I swung through and fired, watching as the falling duck met its reflection slap in the middle of the drain. A rustle at my feet followed by a soft splash told me that Jet was keen to play his part. He was back with the bird in a trice, depositing it at my feet with an uninhibited belch, a shake and a happy wag of that otter-like rudder. No, he did not sit and place it in my hand. I will readily admit that the hound is not of a standard required for gundog tests and competitions, but that's the fault of the

11

owner, not the dog. There are times when fowling, especially on tidal waters with more than one bird down, you need a dog to work using its own initiative. If two birds were drifting tantalisingly away, Jet would always pick the furthest one first, needing no instruction.

I smoothed down the plumage of the shoveler's back admiring the powder blue feathers on the shoulders. It happened to be the first of this species that I had shot for some time. It is a bird that always brings to mind images of the gunners of old, haunting the fen meres, pulk holes and reed beds. Some folk will tell you that they would never eat shoveler, but perhaps that is because they do not fancy anything a little out of the ordinary. I have eaten most types of duck and with very few exceptions, due to what they had been feeding on, found them palatable. I have to say however, that during the first weeks of the season shoveler do have an annoying covering of black down, which is very difficult to remove without skinning the bird. Unless for some reason it is absolutely necessary to skin wildfowl and game I much prefer to leave it on - particularly if the bird is to be roasted.

There was ample time to consider these preferences for it was over an hour before anything else put my shooting skills to the test. It all happened quickly. Suddenly, four mallard were right in front of me, flaring wildly. The first hurried shot fetched one down, but the second shot must have been well behind. As Jet went off to retrieve I stood up to have a stretch and was surprised to find half-a-dozen more duck taking off from the drain a quarter of a mile downwind. They must have dropped in unseen and settled until my shots put them up. Crouching, I watched as the team swung round behind me and came in my direction, surely they were going to pass wide? No, not quite, one turned slightly, enough to bring it just close enough for me to take the shot. The second after I pulled the trigger, the bird sailed over my right shoulder in a lazy arc to thump into the rushes behind me. I watched the others scatter and beat a retreat before looking to pick the fallen duck. It was nowhere to be seen! From the way it had come down I knew that it hadn't walked, but try as I might I could not find that bird. I was still methodically parting patches of rushes in my search when Jet returned with the first duck. He put down this bird, thrust his nose into the vegetation, slightly lower than where I was looking and of course, emerged with the wretched fowl. I felt rather inferior. The look he gave me said it all.

"Here you are old pal, just leave it to the experts."

After the coolness of dawn, the autumn sun became warmer as it gained height. Somehow, the warmth seemed to sharpen the acrid smell of the smoke, still curling from the ejected cartridge cases. The smell, combined with that of the wet dog, stinking of peaty waters and the methane gasses his swimming had released from the mud, would be recognised by any wildfowler. It created a special atmosphere that blended with the general air of rank vegetation, as the pulse of the little world around me slowed in preparation for the coming winter. It was an atmosphere that evoked memories of many other 'Opening Days'. There was no doubt about it - another season had begun.

3

September 15

The weeks that I had expected to drag, as they are prone to do when one eagerly awaits something, by chance passed quickly by. We had been more than usually busy at work and there had not been much time to spend on idle speculation of a sporting nature. Perhaps because my mind had been fully occupied, it seemed that in no time at all I was once again on the way to Norfolk - or as one old friend called it - "The land of milk and honey, the land of barley, bullocks and the folded yow (ewe) flock". I was welcomed by Alec and Molly, who happened to be standing near their gate chatting to a passing neighbour as I drew up. They had been pulling some of their plums and the neighbour departed with a bagful of autumn's early bounty.

After I had deposited my few items of luggage in the spare bedroom we sat down to a very tasty meal of rabbit pie, during which polite conversation was definitely not the order of the day. We were old friends, not embarrassed by silence as we concentrated on the fare before us. Alec did find time between mouthfuls to inform me that the bunny providing our sustenance had left it a bit late to run home to its burrow the previous morning, just as my friend was exercising Rosy on the stubbled headland between some standing corn and the hedge. Alec usually had a gun under his arm on these occasions, as the rabbit had discovered to its cost.

After the meal we relaxed in the small parlour while Alec, for my benefit, went over his plans for the morrow. Molly did not shoot though she turned out on some days and seemed genuinely interested in most rural activities. Just now she poured cups of tea and was obviously steering us away from the whisky bottle. I was not concerned, for with a day's walking in the offing I like to wake up with a clear head, not like a drug addict in need of a fix. My host must have harboured similar thoughts for at around ten o'clock he rose from his chair.

"I don't know about you, but it's an early night for me," he said. When I peeped out of the bedroom window before retiring it was not really dark and the sky seemed fairly clear. Alec was in the yard putting Rosy into her kennel and almost the last thing I heard was the clump of his boots as he came back to the house.

I awoke, filled with keen anticipation of the sport to come. Later, with eggs, bacon and freshly picked mushrooms under our belts we sipped scalding hot, black sugary coffee as we laid out our needs for the day. It was cooler than those oppressive sultry days of August, but it was going to be a warm day all the same and from experience we opted for lightweight clothes whilst sticking to stout leather boots. Rosy had been taking a mild interest in all this, but when the guns and cartridge bags appeared the change in her behaviour was dramatic. She became more and more animated and would not leave us for a moment, just in case that particular moment happened to be the one when we chose to set off. We tipped boxes of Impax sixes into our bags, confident that the ounce load would be ample for the purposes of the day. As we loaded the car our game bags contained some sandwiches and bottles of beer, but we hoped that the contents at the end of the day would be plump and feathered.

The short drive to George's farm passed without incident and before long I was being introduced to our companions for the day. The previous evening Alec had told me that he had invited Leonard, a grocer from the nearest market town and young Tom, George's nephew. George sometimes liked to join the party, but more often than not the various jobs of the farm were more pressing. So it turned out today, while the weather was good they were harvesting potatoes. In fact as we were sorting ourselves out in the farmyard the man himself arrived with a tractor and trailer and a load of potatoes from the field. As he tipped them to be riddled and graded he generously invited us to help ourselves to a few before we left.

Leonard had a couple of springer spaniels that were fussing and sniffing around Rosy, their tails a blur of pent-up excitement. They soon disengaged and became very alert animals as we moved off. The rough plan of campaign was to work inwards from the boundaries of the farm keeping the game as far as possible on our own ground. Naturally this was to prove easier said than done. The stubble of a cut barley field was the first port of call and we began to walk it, keeping the boundary on the left side. The left hand gun, which happened to be Alec, walked a little ahead of the line to encourage any coveys to fly the right way. The springy feel and the sound of the stubble crunching under our boots brought back memories of similar days in previous autumns.

It was a good feeling, one that lasts only a few outings each season before the stubble is ploughed in.

Only one covey of partridges was flushed, but at least they went in the right direction and the line stood still as we watched them down. Towards the end of the field I was alerted by a slight brushing sound in the stubble and turned in time to see a hare darting away from her form. She gave Tom an opportunity and the youngster, with the quick reactions of youth, was up to the challenge. To his shot the hare somersaulted three times and lay still. Young Tom was about to fully understand the irony behind the old saying - 'he who shoots a hare shall carry it.' He didn't seem unduly worried by the banter and when all is said and done, to score with the first shot of the day is always good for the confidence. We came off the stubble and tramped into fifteen acres of sugar beet. Still keeping with the boundary we were on a slight slope and gradually making our way downhill to where a small brook ran through the bottom of the valley. In the thick cover of the beet the spaniels were occasionally confused by the abundance of scent. Three or four times they were obviously hot on a trail and guns were gripped and thumbs lined up on safety catches, but every time the flush came it was pheasants, not partridges that jumped. More often than not they were only half-grown pheasants that squeaked as they fled. It was warm work striding through the beet and I think we were all relieved when we left it. The next field was one of standing corn with the headlands cut. Halfway along the stubble a large covey that had sat tight suddenly erupted, almost at our feet. Feathered shapes hurtled in all directions and after the long period with no legitimate quarry showing itself they almost caught us unawares. Even so I managed to drop a right and left and when the dust had settled, found that another four partridges had fallen to the salvo. The dogs were busy for a few moments before we resumed our walk. A little further on, the spaniels tore off into the standing corn. The party stood, following their progress by way of the waving corn stems. When the birds were flushed and this time they were partridges, they were easily over a hundred yards away. Once again though, they veered right. Tom was right-hand gun and so nearer the standing corn. When we reached the end of the block he peered round.

"Will you look at that!" he exclaimed. We looked. Fifty or sixty partridges, several coveys mingling and combining together were running, heads erect, along the edge of the block. On flushing, they flew obligingly, towards the roots so we carried on with anticipation. Another, smaller stubble field was to be crossed before we took a right-angled turn to follow the brook along. After witnessing the mass exodus it surprised no one when nothing was flushed from this particular stubble. Even so we ought not to have been lulled into the carelessness that followed. Part of Alec's grand plan was to caché our lunches in one of the piles of straw bales on the field and leave the bottles of beer in the cool waters of the brook. Alec unloaded and put down his gun while he went to take the beer down to the brook. The rest of us stood waiting for him with broken guns. The moment he stepped down over the brink we heard an exclamation followed by a flurry of wings and an urgent quack. The best part of a score of wild duck hurried off and they almost made it without a shot being fired. Len, who was nearest to them, managed to snap shut his gun and get off a longish shot. An outside bird shut its wings and fell spectacularly, but we were all thinking that had we been more careful we would have walked right onto them. Len's bird proved to be a drake with traces of the chestnut breast and green head of its winter plumage already beginning to show. As an experienced wildfowler Alec was able to show Len and young Tom how you can sex a mallard even in the full summer plumage, by checking the white wing bars. Those of the drake stop level with the brilliant blue of the speculum, whereas those of the duck extend beyond the blue feathers.

That little educational interlude over, the party walked inwards, heading for two fields of potatoes that lay adjacent to each other. Lining out we set off across the rows, pushing through the tangled haulms that had been sprayed to kill them off. Now dead and brittle, they snapped dustily against our boots. The atmosphere was electric as every second every one of us expected the sudden whirr! whirr! whirr! of the flushed covey. Paradoxically, when it did come it was almost a shock. It was certainly no place for a man with a weak heart. Often the lower corners of the fields, where reeds had invaded the potato crop, gave up coveys that burst up in a cloud of dust. Shots rang out and feathers flew; the line froze like statues as excited dogs ran in. Most birds escaped, but enough fell to make our game bags begin to outweigh the cartridge bags. It was a beaming team that ambled back to the brook to take lunch. Sitting leaning back against the bales of straw we munched our way through the cheese and onion sandwiches, pork pies and beer whilst attempting to reconstruct a blow by blow account of the morning. Taking care to keep clear of the straw, pipes were lit and another ten minutes of banter was enjoyed. There was gentle leg pulling about the easy bird that was missed and the young pheasant that almost wasn't.

We were all pretty warm and with lunch doing little to alleviate the general lethargy, the afternoon's activities were of a less optimistic nature than originally planned. A few more dusty acres of potatoes and golden stubbles were

19

walked and one or two more partridges added to the bag. For a finale Alec had planned a mini-drive. The potato field that was being harvested lay in front of a blackthorn hedge. It was after half past three so the workers had gone home. This meant that we could shoot here confident in the knowledge that nobody was in the line of fire. Two guns would stand behind the hedge while the other two beat through the remaining potatoes towards them. The toss of a coin decided that Len and Tom were to be the standing guns. They did a wide detour to bring them behind the hedge without disturbing any game. While they were thus occupied Alec said.

"When we act as beaters it goes without saying that we leave birds that are going forward, but any that go out to either side are ours. You take anything that goes out to the right." Once Len and Tom were in position we moved into the potatoes. Again there was that excitement of bracing oneself for the sudden flush, which never fades no matter how often you repeat it. A few yards in and a covey sprang up to Alec's left, one falling to his shot. Then three partridges, bigger birds, Frenchmen they were; got up right in front of me going straight for the hedge. I held my fire and watched. They topped the hedge, wings curved down in that deceptively quick flight. Bang! Bang! One bird folded, fell and that was it. It wasn't much of a drive perhaps, but for all that, the little strategy had worked and was well worth the effort if the look on Tom's face was anything to go by. It was Tom who had taken the shots and it was his first red-legged partridge to boot. An unexpected bonus came my way as we walked out of the potatoes. There, in one of the rows sat three mushrooms, two of which were the size of dinner plates. I was not long in adding them to my game-bag.

We returned to the farmyard where the bag was laid out and shared among the party who made sure that George was included. Ten brace plus the duck and the hare was deemed a good day's sport by a weary but contented band of guns before they parted to return to their respective homes. Back at the cottage, after we had washed and freshened up I thanked my friends for their hospitality and asked Alec if he would like to come over to my place the following weekend for a run out to the marsh. I have to say I wasn't in the least bit surprised by his reply.

4

September 23

The hands of the clock were just about on eleven. I was sitting in the kitchen drinking what I considered to be a well-deserved mug of tea when I heard the crunch of car tyres on the gravel outside. Guessing the identity of my caller I didn't bother to get up, but reached for another mug and filled it from the teapot. The kitchen door opened and Alec's cheery face peered round the frame.

"You are here then," he grinned.

"You must have smelt this," I retorted, pointing to his mug. Whilst we enjoyed the tea we talked over last week's partridge shoot and I gently pulled my friend's leg for blundering in on those duck.

"I must be getting old, I wouldn't have been so careless a few years ago as well you know. Still, good luck to them. We didn't deserve to get them that easily," he said smiling good-naturedly.

Draining our mugs, we ambled out into the yard to collect his baggage from his little car. It was an old, but well maintained, Ford Popular. I reminded Alec of his threats in previous seasons to issue freight charges if he was going to ferry my double eight-bore down to the marsh as well as the two of us. He laughed at the memory and said.

"I hope you don't mind, I have brought some extra freight myself today - I've brought Rosy with me." Assuring him that Rosy was more than welcome I carried his holdall into the house, where we ate a light lunch prior to setting off for our afternoon of sport.

The drive from my house to the Lincolnshire coast of The Wash took about forty-five minutes. It would have taken quite a bit longer in Alec's car for he never drove it much above 30 mph no matter how clear the road. Besides which, we rarely met much traffic on those straight and isolated roads across the fen. The roads got narrower and lonelier the nearer we got to our destination. The only homes were farm-houses, including some very substantial dwellings, reflecting the well-earned rewards reaped by the families who had worked this rich land for generations. Pheasants strutted around the grounds like domestic fowl; a fact that did not pass unnoticed by certain local poachers.

So, we arrived at a famous corner of Holbeach Marsh and having arrived we parked the car under the sea wall at a point where it formed a small vee-shaped bay. Here a large creek ran out parallel to the far arm of the sea wall for quite a way, before it meandered its own course away out through the saltings. The saltings were extensive on this particular marsh and consisted mostly of the sage-coloured crab grass so familiar on this coast, with patches of shorter grass and samphire dotted here and there. Where the vegetation petered out, the stiff stalked sea asters were more prevalent, some with the remains of flowers on them. Having donned our thigh boots and cartridge belts Alec and I walked along the sea wall to the right. The wall marched off into the distance, taking a remarkably straight line with only an occasional bend. The land behind it was a patchwork of pale yellow stubble fields with various shades of dark green where potatoes and sugar beet were growing. The potatoes were being taken up and one or two harvesters could be seen slowly moving across the fields, each with its gang of women grading the crop, whilst throwing off the stones and clots of earth from the moving belts. It was the small potatoes and some not so small that were left on the fields after the harvest. These remained on the surface after the next crop had been drilled, usually winter wheat. Later, after a frost, they would rot and become an attractive larder for hungry mallard. Even some of the beet fields had already had the roots from the corners pulled and heaped to allow access for the beet harvesters next month.

After half an hour of brisk walking, with Rosy hunting the bankside grasses we came to the point where we needed to leave the sea wall and strike out across the marsh. Some five hundred yards out there was a chain of small mounds, which in fact were the remains of a low bank with several breaches in it. The further we went, the fewer the gaps until the bank ran continuously, bearing right to run parallel with the main sea-wall. This bank was an important part of the strategy of the day. The tides, after the new moon, were at their highest. Our plan was to hide at the edge of the marsh to await the tide and the expected mass movement of waders that the flood would provoke, then to retreat before it to the sanctuary of the bank.

The temperatures of late summer had lingered into September and by the time we split up to take up our positions I was feeling pretty hot under the collar. Even light jackets are warm after a long walk and thigh boots are cumbersome at the best of times. I filled my bag with crab grass and sat on the side of a gutter with my feet down in it. The thick vegetation at this time of year offered very good cover. There was time to fill a pipe and to quietly contemplate my surroundings, with eyes and ears alert for any sudden movement or sound. Three-quarters of a mile away I spotted something moving. It turned out to be another wildfowler steadily making his way out for the flight. I mentally wished him luck, but at the same time hoped that any shots he had would send fowl in our direction.

I had tapped out my pipe on my palm, (On the marshes you don't tap it on your heel, which by now is well coated with mud) perhaps no more than ten minutes, before I felt the first gentle surge of the tide push against my boots as it came gurgling purposefully up the gutters, runnels and creeks. Perhaps a quarter of a mile away out over the mud I could already discern the thin line of dirty scum riding the vanguard of the sea, which with a sinister hiss, was approaching over the flats faster than walking pace. Before and along it flew flight upon flight, pack upon twisting pack of waders all with one aim, to take a little more food before the supply was cut off for a few hours. By far the largest parties were made up of knot. Hundreds, sometime thousands of birds, dull brown then suddenly shining white as they changed direction and showed their undersides, the changing colour moving along the flock like a Mexican wave in a sports stadium.

The redshank seemed to prefer the creeks in the saltings, but there were certainly some meeting the tide as well as curlew, godwits, oystercatchers and others of the hen-footed fowl. A few birds began to fly towards the land, presenting us with the occasional chance of a shot, but it was when the tide was within a hundred yards of us that we really found ourselves in the thick of things, at least for a few hectic moments. I was about to swing the gun onto a grey plover when I spotted, just in time, a spring of teal hurtling by about six feet above the mud. My double shot sent one spinning down to splash into the shallow waters. I looked round for Rosy, but I need not have fretted for she didn't miss much. The bitch was already bounding towards my bird sending up billows of spray until she ran into a submerged creek. Rosy made nothing of that. She was soon out on the other side and seconds later was on the return swim, with the teal safely in that velvety mouth. In the time taken for the retrieve we were washed out by the tide and had to move back onto the low bank where we hid in the long coarse grass for the remainder of the flight. Curlew flying in to sit out the tide on the quiet stubble fields beyond the sea wall were our main quarry, but they did not all come kindly. Most were wide, but we were by no means out of it, some even followed the line of the bank. I watched fascinated as one of these parties steadily beat up to where I knew Alec was hidden. Surely he must shoot soon? Was he looking the wrong way? This was unlikely as most of the birds were coming from one direction only. Then the curlew, there were about eight or nine of them, flared as Alec came suddenly into partial view. One curlew folded, another collapsed tipping backwards and as they fell the sound of the twin reports reached me. So absorbed was I watching my friend in action that an opportunity was almost lost. Out of the corner of my eye a movement high overhead attracted my attention. A line of long winged, long billed waders sped along the shore. Bar-tailed godwits, heading only the Lord knew where. The single shot I took pulled one down in a most spectacular fashion. I hoped that Alec was watching.

The tide was well past our refuge now, but we had deliberately allowed ourselves to be marooned. Our sport was over for the day as the fowl had fled before the flood. Between our bank and the sea wall the broad waters rippled and shone and sparkled in the September afternoon sun. We had a wait of a couple of hours or so before the tide ebbed enough to allow our retreat, but we were in no hurry. Laying out our bag we sorted through the birds stroking the feathers smooth and looking for any unusual markings or peculiarities. Respect for the slain is very important; they should never be stuffed willy-nilly into a bag without due care and attention. Six curlew, eight knots, three godwits, three grey plover and of course my teal were duly inspected and then laid among the grass in a patch of shade. None were ringed, nor gave any reason for particular comment except one of the curlew, which was on the heavy side.

It was warm in the sun, and now that we were relaxing, I felt the corners of my eyes prickling as if irritated by hay fever. Could it have been the effect of late pollen from some of the marsh vegetation blown on the breeze? Whatever it was it was bearable and after producing pipes and tobacco we lit up whilst leaning back against the grassy bank to await release from our temporary exile.

5

September 23ii

On our return from the coast Alec fed and watered Rosy while I braced up the birds as far as was practical and hung them in the cool of an outbuilding that at one time had been the washhouse. Although no longer used, the copper with its brick fireplace was still intact and always brought back memories of my childhood. In those days one of my pocket money jobs was to feed a similar copper fire with broken wooden boxes, cardboard or anything else that it would consume, in order to heat the water for our bath night or mother's weekly washday. With the imagined smell of steam still lingering in my nostrils I went back into the house for a quick wash and brush up before rustling up a meal.

I had arranged with a friend for us to try one of his barley stubbles in the evening and just after a quarter-past-seven Rosy looked on in amazement as we loaded our guns and bags once more into the car. Well, let's say she looked on for a few seconds before she leapt into the car and peered out under the tailgate with an expression that said, "All right, what are we waiting for?" It didn't matter whose car it was, if a gun went into it so did Rosy. Fifteen minutes later the car was being driven slowly and with care along a dirt drove bordered on either side by deep, water filled dykes. The surface of the drove was hard enough, but the wheels of tractors and farm machinery had left, in places, deep ruts. These had to be straddled or else there was a serious risk of ripping off our exhaust with my low clearance.

"Should have bought a Land Rover!" quipped Alec. The suggestion had its merits I had to admit, but it was surprising where the old motor could go with a little careful navigation. However, even at dead slow there was plenty of dust and I was thankful that most of it stayed on the outside, which did not used to happen with an earlier vehicle I had owned!

When our targeted stubble field was still two fields away we left the car to walk down to it. The straw had been baled and carted, leaving the field as bare and flat as a billiard table. The boundary at the far end was a deep dyke with about five feet width of water along its length. As for the neighbouring fields, one was another stubble and the other was a healthy looking crop of sugar beet. Half a score of woodpigeon clattered up as we walked along the dyke side between the two stubbles. This dyke was dry like the one running parallel on the far side of the field. One rarely sees any water at all in these dykes and I think they now serve to mark the boundaries of the fields as much as any past drainage purpose, though in extremely wet times they are still part of the system. They certainly take up a lot less land than a hedge, which on this valuable peat soil is more than a minor consideration. Another poignant point in their favour was that they provide excellent hiding places for the sportsman on occasions like this one.

I knew a few duck had been using the field, indeed we found some brown mallard feathers near the spot the pigeons had recently vacated, but I had not had time to visit during the past four days, so we were really just taking potluck. There was no 'hot-spot' as far as I knew so we decided to hedge our bets and take a dyke on either side in which to await proceedings. We selected our respective places some three hundred yards diagonally apart across the barley stubble. I pressed down the grasses and nettles to make a hollow and, to start with at least, sat on my game bag with my back against the low bank. As I made myself comfortable, I remembered that not many hours had passed since I was ensconced in a similar position on that bank on the marsh. Behind, my field of vision was pretty well unrestricted, while to the front the horizon was the top of the beet. The low September sun was still very warm to the face and I made the most of it while idly scanning the horizon. Nevertheless, knowing that later on the evening could well be several degrees cooler, I had donned a green sweater as a simple camouflage, with an ancient tweed jacket lying ready should it be required.

A whistle from Alec caused me to turn sharply. After a moment I picked up a movement in the sky a quarter of a mile away, specks only at first, but specks in the familiar pattern known to every fowler. The specks developed as expected into a small team of duck, which were approaching very quickly indeed. It was not our lot to have so jammy a start and it soon became obvious that the duck were going to pass over well out of shot. Nevertheless we kept well down, determined not to betray our position. As the team came up I kept them in view under the brim of my cap. Mallard they were, the sun illuminating their plumage so that each bird appeared in sharp focus. It was a grand sight and an encouraging one too. I watched them until they banked suddenly and glided down four fields away.

Another hour passed - surely we ought to see some movement soon? It was getting cooler now, but it wasn't the temperature that caused me to pull on my jacket. Myriad mosquitoes had emerged from nowhere and now hung in dancing, infuriating clouds all along the dyke. Their attention focused particularly, or so it seemed, around my ruddy head. In later years, various insect repellent creams and sprays would come on the market, but at the time in question it was a matter of turning up the coat collar, pulling on the gloves and reaching for your pipe! A good fug of pungent tobacco smoke really does do the trick, but the downside is that you cannot carry on smoking bowl after bowl without ending up with a stinking headache. At least it keeps the little blighters away for a reasonable time so that one can concentrate on the job in hand.

A sudden whistle of wing beats, but from behind and the duck had passed before I could raise the gun. Then a couple of reports from Alec's hiding place. Peering through the shadows I could just make out a vague smudge rapidly departing. Turning back to look at the western sky, which was now a band of soft orange, I was only just in time to see a single black shape with wings flickering almost as fast as a bee's. The hurried first shot was well wide, but as the duck swerved the second barrel found its mark and the long neck flung back as the bird was lost to sight in the gloom. Seconds later came that satisfying thump that is so familiar to the stubble field shooter.

I found the mallard without difficulty, but as I hurried back towards my hollow a pack of teal, some thirty of them, swept right over it and only six feet above the ground. I could see every bird clearly and although if I had been back in position

31

they might well have taken me by surprise, I naturally did not think of that at the time. I just scurried on quickly and got down out of sight. A trio of short-eared owls turned up and amused themselves for a while by circling my head and making low level passes. Eventually they got bored and moved on across the field. I happened to be looking in the direction of Alec when a sudden stab of orange focused my eye. The sound of the shot followed almost instantaneously. It seemed that my friend was in business again. Not long afterwards the light faded. Pinions continued to whistle overhead, but the mallard flew by unseen. In the very last of the light I spotted a team of five drop in to the far side of the adjacent stubble field. Moments later another pair followed them in. Well, we would be leaving them without further disturbance this night. I heard Alec's boots brushing through the stubble as he made his way across the field to join me. He was preceded by Rosy who arrived several seconds before him with a wagging tail and a happy demeanour.

"How did you get on?" Alec asked, when he caught up with his bitch. I held up my duck.

"I knew you had at least one, I heard it thump down. I got a right and left out of a gang of twenty, they came in beautifully, but I missed that last one. I should have had it really, but it was too good for me."

We crunched back to the motor to rock and roll back along the drove trying very hard not to take off the exhaust pipe in the process. It seemed no time at all before we were home and after the long day in the open air I fell sound asleep almost as soon as my head touched the pillow.

6

September 24

A pleasant breeze wafted in through the bedroom window when I awoke. My wife and I had breakfast together before she went off to visit her mother; I then knocked on the door of the spare room. Satisfied by sounds from within indicating that Alec was rousing himself, I went down for another cup of coffee.

"You should have got me up earlier," mumbled Alec as he entered the kitchen.

"Oh you're all right," I replied, "nothing's spoiling. We'll get off when you've had a bite to eat."

We planned to try a marsh to the south of where we were yesterday, just on the Lincolnshire side of the county's border with Norfolk. The sole reason for was the fact that on a Sunday we could legally shoot on our side of the county line, but not on the other.

From my house the distance was about the same, we merely pointed the car in a Northeasterly direction instead of Northwesterly. We traversed the flat fens, mile after mile of level landscape. For a time the road took us along the top of the bank of a tidal river, the water flowing sluggishly between shelves of mud, still shining where the tide had recently left it. Some redshank ran along the mud not far from a pair of shelduck. Farther along stood a heron in the time-honoured pose of static alertness. I wouldn't give much for the chances of any careless eel or butt that ventured within range of that dagger of a beak. On the other side of our passing car the bank fell away to the land some twenty feet below. Even while driving along it was obvious that the river level was well above that of the land. Many folk, including some who have lived in the fen district for years, remain blissfully unaware that thousands of acres of rich arable land and the residents of countless villages and towns owe their continued existence to the daily works and maintenance by the Internal Drainage Boards. Without the constant vigilance of the drainage engineers and their staff monitoring levels and pumping when appropriate, miles of fenland could so very easily slip back into an environment of bog and swamp.

Presently we crossed the river entering an even less populated area. Here the soil was silt as opposed to the black peat lands that we had left. The square tower of a village church was behind us when almost immediately the public roads turned into concrete tracks, many of which were laid down during the Second World War. Over a nineteenth century sea wall, we motored and on again through fields of stubble, potatoes and sugar beet. Yet another sea wall was crossed, this time not above fifty years old and after driving over the land that had subsequently been reclaimed, we pitched up right under the grassy bank of the current barrier to the sea.

Five minutes later we mounted the bank and scanned the wide vista of marshes with our glasses. This being the Wash coast with a tide not due for several hours, the sea was out of sight. Between La Mer and our thigh boots was mile after mile of mud, eventually blending with another world of sandbanks and mussel scaups - The world of seals, cockle fishermen and nighttime roosting pink-footed geese. The salt marshes blanketed the mud along the coast in a fringe varying from a couple of hundred yards to perhaps a quarter of a mile at this particular spot. There was some similarity to moorland heather and it was at least as difficult to walk through. No other humans, indeed no birds nor anything else in sight, except the endless sage-green terrain. To the uninitiated the whole place would appear to be utterly lifeless, but of course we knew differently.

Pushing through the stiff stalked crab grass and jumping narrow gutters we headed out across the marsh until we came to one of the larger creeks that meander out to the bare mud. The bottoms of such creeks are usually firm enough to enable good wading, but getting into them can be a different matter, even for the experienced creek crawler. It is best to slide down the muddy banks, or at least spread your weight a bit. If your leg slips thigh-deep into the mud it is very difficult to extract and more often than not you can say goodbye to your boot! No matter what you do, it's a pretty muddy business. I managed to slither down comparatively cleanly and gleefully watched Alec's descent. Almost at the bottom he sank one foot to just below the knee and I tried hard not to let him hear me laughing quietly as he struggled to free himself. The trouble was the more he struggled and swore the funnier it became. By the time he was ready to move on, my sides were fairly aching and he gave me a look that sent the wordless message; "Your turn will come old friend, your turn will come."

I led off, following the winding, seemingly aimless, wanderings of the creek. At each bend we peered round - just in case. Smaller creeks ran into ours and when we came to these, one or the other of us would clamber up to check ahead with the glasses. It is not often that you catch the old curlew off guard. The merest hint of a head showing above the mud would send them away, screeching in alarm, putting everything on the alert over a wide area. If we did spot some curlew in the distance and one of us could retrace our steps to skirt round in another creek, there would be an opportunity of a pincer movement whereby I might manage to push the birds over Alec or vice-versa.

No such chance presented itself this morning, so we pushed on along our creek. At first the saltings were three feet above our heads so that anything flying over was within close quarters the moment it was seen. This fact did not necessarily mean an easy shot however, and a few misses were recorded. As we got closer to the mud, the creeks became shallower. Here we were able to spy out over the marsh without clambering up, but we would have to crouch to remain hidden. When shots were fired they often put up other birds. If they were curlew and not too far away, say three hundred yards, Alec had a clever ruse to decoy them. He would wave his hat just above the marsh grass and suddenly withdraw it. The effect was remarkable. Curlew that were going to pass out of range sometimes twisted and turned to investigate. It reminded me of a cat which cannot resist if you attract its attention with a twig from behind a tree, when you keep the twig out of sight for a few seconds Puss will pounce. The curlew perhaps thought it was another of its clan dropping in for a feed. The trick did not always work, but it worked often enough to make it worth a try.

We splashed our way out until we reached the bare mud. Our spell on the marsh had brought short bursts of excitement and long periods when nothing moved. We returned by way of another creek and had some fun with a few redshank, which came yelping over our heads. They were by no means as easy as they looked, often jinking like snipe at the critical moment. We were both engrossed with wading a tricky bend when something hurtled past very low and obviously following the line of the creek.

"What the devil was that? It's a duck of some sort." Alec exclaimed.

"It was a shoveler." I replied. "I caught sight of its bill as it almost took my right ear off!"

There was no explanation as to why the shoveler had flown in. The tide might have begun to flow, but it was too early for that to move duck. More than likely it was merely a whim on the bird's part.

It would be hours before we could expect a tide flight and besides Alec had to get back home, so we returned to my house with three curlew and three redshank to add to the bag already hanging in the washhouse. Alec took what birds he wanted and even as his car pulled out into the road en-route for Norfolk, I set about plucking and cleaning some of the rest. Even in the cool days of winter I seldom hang duck or geese for more than a week and it is usually too warm in September to hang wildfowl for long unless you have no sense of smell at all. I have to admit though that the best curlew I have ever eaten had been hanging for at least a fortnight, but I didn't prepare that one!

7

September 30

Not far from my house there lived an elderly widow who was always ready to accept a bird or two. Her late, lamented husband had been a wildfowler of the old school so she knew all about the preparation of fowl for the table. During the week I had delivered to her the three redshanks and one of the curlew from last weekend's bag. She laid them on the scrubbed pine of the kitchen table. "I shall pluck these straight away and put them all together in a pie. That'll make a couple of meals for me; I don't eat a great deal these days. Will you take some beans? They're nearly finished now, but there should be enough for a bait," she said. That gesture was typical of her generation. They would not feel comfortable in accepting a gift unless they could offer you something in return and yet they were always generous with their own largesse without thought for recompense. We had, in the various seasons, received pounds of strawberries and raspberries, tomatoes and sundry vegetables from the good lady. Needless to say I made sure that she was never short of a plump pheasant, mallard or the occasional leveret. On the day in question while I was pulling the last of the beans I had another look at the ancient gunning punt that lay, where it had lain for the past fifteen years, upside down in the lee of a greenhouse. Both punt and greenhouse were rotting derelicts that before long would disintegrate and crumble. I idly wondered how many duck had been tucked under the gunwales of the long slender boat during her long working life, how many stones of eels had wriggled and squirmed on her bottom boards on humid summer nights of long ago.

We had eaten the other two curlews the previous day and very tasty they were too. September and October are the best months for these long-billed waders to be palatable; once we are into November I do not care for them as a table bird.

My thoughts turning to duck, I decided to return to the stubble we had visited last week, but it was raining steadily as I drove to the farm. It was still quite early and as there was no point in getting soaked I turned down an intersecting track, which led to the wide dyke running along the boundary. At the end of the track was an earth bridge, piped with a culvert to allow the free passage of water. I could park the car on the bridge and hidden by the rails of a fence sit in the dry and observe unseen, the comings and goings of any duck in the vicinity.

The rain changed to showers, but there were wave after wave of them blowing up from a sky that was grey with low, impenetrable cloud. It would stop drizzling for perhaps five minutes giving one slight cause for optimism only to be followed by another downpour. This could go on until dark! A movement in the grass caught my eye, a hundred yards away a hare came loping along. I kept an eye on her and she kept coming in my general direction, stopping every now and again before moving on again. Eventually she was within ten feet of the car where she stopped to nibble some grass. Her ears cocked up and she sat up on her hind legs looking as bedraggled as a drowned rat, but the inclement weather did not seem to bother her unduly. She must have noticed that the car was alien to the normal scene for in an instant she was a different animal. Gone was the slow lolloping beast and in its stead a grey-brown blur speeding away in a mist of spray sent up by those swift legs brushing through the sodden grasses.

One pair of duck came in, approaching the drain with intent, but for reasons best known to themselves, they changed their minds at the last moment and cleared off again. Four more crossed the drain in distant view, skirting low over the fields, but due to the poor visibility I soon lost sight of them. A large dark bird appeared from the opposite direction slowly flapping and then gliding on powerful wings; a marsh harrier, female by the look of it, but it was difficult to identify in the gloom. About ten minutes later another followed on the same line. I suppose it could have been the same bird, but if so it would have had to made a very wide circuit around me.

Just on dusk the rain stopped, so I hurried along the side of the drain to a spot some six hundred yards from the car. It wasn't long before mist began to rise, creating a waist-high blanket that gave the scene an eerie effect. I suppose it must have provided good cover, but my theory was never put to the test. All I heard was a single mallard and a small pack of wigeon. The latter could not have been far off, but I could not see them and they flew on whistling joyously in search of an evening meal. I walked back to the car with clean barrels, but my luck was not entirely out for as I unlocked the vehicle the rain returned and this time it did not stop.

The windscreen wipers were in action during the entire homeward journey. I have known far worse driving conditions, but I was not sorry when my house hove into view. I was even happier after I had fed the dog and cleaned my gun, because I was looking forward to the supper of cold partridge that awaited my attention. Later on my wife and I would sit on either side of the empty hearth and go over the events of the day while Jet would lie across my feet, snoring like a nestling barn owl.

8

October 6

It was a couple of weeks before Alec and I shared any further sport. I had been out for a few afternoons to walk around the sugar beet fields of a farmer friend, but this early in the season it is a matter of pushing through acres and acres of the crop only to flush half-grown birds. With perseverance one can usually put a brace of mature cock birds into the bag before the afternoon is over.

I was in the bath on Thursday evening when the telephone sent its strident summons echoing through the house. My wife came in to tell me that it was Alec and should she tell him I would ring him back? Sensing sport in the offing I quickly wrapped a towel around my waist and dripped my way to the instrument.

"Ha you a' flooding the house out boy?" came the cheeky enquiry as I pressed the receiver to my ear. Without waiting for a response, Alec went on.

"George's neighbour has got a lot of geese coming into his water meadows in the mornings. They are making a mess and he wants them shifting. I'm going to have a crack them on Saturday morning - care to join me?"

Receiving a quick and very much to the point response to this enquiry my friend laughed.

"Good, come over tomorrow so we can get an early start in the morning. Better still, if you can be at my place by three o'clock tomorrow afternoon we might just have some fun then." Alec did not go into details and I didn't ask. I simply confirmed that I would indeed arrive by fifteen hundred hours.

As a matter of fact, because of a variety of reasons I pitched up half an hour earlier than the appointed hour. I knew that that would not bother either my host or his wife. On the contrary Alec hailed me with enthusiasm even before I had opened the door of the car.

"I'm glad you're early, I want to get off straight away - or at least as soon as you've dropped your bag off in the kitchen."

Without asking for an explanation I walked to the cottage, handed my holdall to a beaming Molly at the kitchen door and hurried back to her spouse.

"Just bring your gun and some sixes," instructed Alec. Obediently, I emptied a box of number-six shot cartridges into the side pockets of my jacket and clambered into the ancient Ford. As we trundled along the empty lanes, Alec briefed me as to the purpose of our hasty mission.

"I was walking up old Fred's stubbles the other afternoon and all of a sudden seemingly out of no-where, a pigeon flight materialised. The next day I was in the car, but passing about the same time and the same thing happened - almost spot on four o'clock. I thought we'd try to intercept them, always assuming they turn up today."

A reed filled ditch ran along one headland of the stubble field and it was here that Alec proposed that we should wait in ambush. There was a fairly strong wind blowing from behind us, which was an encouraging advantage. We took up our positions one hundred yards apart. There was not a bird to be seen apart from a covey of partridges making their way in an unhurried fashion towards some cover at the far end of the stubble. I was beginning to think it was third time *un*lucky when three woodpigeon flew in low from the front. They passed out of range and I looked at my watch, the hands stood at three minutes past four. I chuckled to myself and peered through the fringe of reeds, not really all that surprised to see more pigeons bearing down on us. Not all came near enough of course, but even as out of range birds passed, more could be seen half a mile away, travelling across the flat fields and coming in our direction. We began to get some shooting. At first I made the mistake of getting the gun up too soon, while the birds were well in front. As they flared on seeing me the wind was strong enough to push them back out of range. After that, I allowed them to come right in, sometimes even letting them pass before taking the shot. The flight lasted for only about fifteen minutes - but what a fifteen minutes! Guns swinging up at the last moment, puffs of grey feathers suddenly appearing and being quickly dispersed by the wind as birds crumpled and fell, staggered and whirled down. Once a pack of twenty straggled by and three spun out to the first shot. On ejecting the fired cases I discovered that I had loaded one barrel with a goose cartridge by mistake. My old magnum always did throw a good pattern of number threes! The last lot of pigeons departed and we began the pick-up. Alec thought they were heading to roost in a wood about a mile further on. As most of our birds had fallen on the stubble field picking up was easy. The tally was twenty-five shared almost equally between us. As I gathered the last half-dozen Alec went off for the car and moments later appeared driving over the field to transport the bag home. It had been a short flight, but our barrels had been more than a little warm. The wisdom of taking opportunities as they are presented was borne out in by our adventure. When we next met, Alec told me that two days later the flight line had dried up.

Later that evening we sauntered down to the "Blue Boar" where George had arranged to meet us. He was already in the bar and halfway down his pint of mild. After the landlord had drawn off pints of bitter for us we discussed the plans for the morning.

"I hope you'll trim some of them old geese up," said George, "They're driving poor old Edgar mad."

We assured him that we would do our best to send out the right message to the uninvited guests.

9

October 7

George's neighbour, known to one and all as Uncle Edgar, owned some meadows that ran down to a river at a point where it curved round in a long bend. His cattle rotated from one pasture to another. A couple of hundred geese could and did consume a lot of grass in a relatively short period of grazing and much of what they did not eat, they fouled with their droppings. Alec and I had collected young Tom, George's nephew on the way and now we sat in the car at the field gate watching for any early movement. It was 7.30 and well light, but Alec explained that the marauding geese roosted on a large lake about a mile away and that at this time of the year, unlike truly wild geese, they were not particularly early risers. In fact they had not been turning up until 8.30 or even 9.00 am in recent days, when Alec had put in some time on recognisance.

There was certainly neither sign nor sound of geese as we pulled out guns and bags from the car prior to moving off. The land fell away fairly steeply towards the river and thick thorn hedges, dotted with the occasional tree, separated each meadow. At the bottom of the slope the river was hidden from view for the time being by a thick blanket of grey-white mist, though this would soon evaporate as the temperature rose. We had decided to cover two of the meadows, which had been heavily grazed by the geese. Alec knew the general direction from which the skeins of birds would come, but with scarcely a breath of wind, not even so much as a breeze to help us, it was difficult to judge where they would pitch into our chosen meadows. In the end we decided to copper both bets and take up positions on either side of the hedge that ran between the two meadows. I had brought some camouflaged netting so I chose to stay on the side where we thought the geese would come. The other two, opting to rely on the hedge for cover, went through the gate and walked lower down the slope on the far side. Alec headed down to the river in case geese happened to drop in there before feeding. I have no doubt that it crossed his mind that he might also get an opportunity for a shot at a passing duck. Tom had settled behind the hedge about halfway between us.

As we had come for geese I had borrowed Alec's Greener ten-bore, which he claimed threw a pretty good pattern of Number 1 shot and was deadly if the bearer was up to the job. I stood it, unloaded, against the hedge while I sorted out my netting. I had hardly pulled the net from my bag before the cattle grazing in the field had become inquisitive, and sauntered over to investigate this stranger in their territory. It wasn't long before twenty or thirty heavily breathing beasts surrounded me. Annoyed at first, I set about ignoring them, apart from warding off frothy nosed attempts to lick my coat. After a while they settled down, flicking their tails and coughing. It suddenly dawned on me that if the cattle stayed put, I had the perfect hide. What was more natural a sight for the geese to see here than a herd of cattle? I picked up the gun and after checking that no twigs had fallen into the barrels, slipped in a couple of cartridges.

Jackdaws went noisily about their business and once, a long strung out party of rooks clamoured their way to the day's chosen feeding grounds. I noticed that every now and then single woodpigeon, or perhaps sometimes a pair, flew passed a certain tall beech on the far side of the meadow. It was obviously some kind of a landmark for them and enough pigeons flew within range of that tree to have made it worthwhile for some knowledgeable local, to wait there one morning. A soft fluttering sound caused me to turn and a flock of tiny birds came jinking along the hedge - eight, nine, ten, twelve long-tailed tits, all soft shades of pink, black and white - never still for a second. I was gazing after the delightful little creatures as they passed my hiding place, when the yaffling call of a green woodpecker broke the silence. I didn't see it, but Tom said later that it flew across the river and came right over his head. Then came the faint sound of geese on the wing. So faint that at first I wondered if my ears were playing tricks, but there was no doubt as a skein of forty greylags came into view over the trees on the other side of the field. They immediately turned as though intending to glide down right in front of me, but changed their minds and lifted again to cross the hedge fifty yards to my right. They were thirty-five yards up and still climbing when I swung onto a goose well back in the skein. At the shot it's neck flung back and the bird plummeted down to thump on the turf. My living 'hide' stampeded off, a welter of flying cloven hooves and divots of mud. I was so concerned that my goose would be trampled underfoot that I did not fire the second barrel. Luckily, the cattle went clear of the bird, which turned out to be a nice little goose, whose notched tail feathers indicated that it was a bird of the year, and therefore ought to be tender on the table.

Later, I would show the tail to Tom, and mention that by the time geese and duck have reached maturity, the tail feathers have grown to a point. As a guide to the age of a shot fowl, it's a useful bit of knowledge. I would also advise the youngster that it is a good idea to avoid shooting the leading geese in the party, unless you need a new sole for your shoes. It does however, take an experienced hand to remember this when a skein of geese are thrashing overhead.

The skein naturally made themselves scarce after fleeing my assault and did not offer a shot to the others. The mist had lifted from the river by now and the waterway could be seen meandering leadenly through other meadows into the distance. Half an hour later twenty geese arrived and pitched with a flurry of wings out in the middle of the field. They began feeding at once, slowly grazing their way down the slope, strong necks and bills cropping the grass with a sideways motion. Would they stay out in the middle? If more came, would they not join them? I had begun to wonder if I could somehow get round behind them and drive them over Alec and Tom. I had dismissed the idea, as I would have been seen the moment I had twitched a muscle. Our next move however, was decided for us. Another skein of greys swung in from over the river and our lot jumped to join them. Back towards the river went the whole lot and I could see that at least one of my friends was going to get a shot. It was exciting to see the enormous birds beating ever on towards the hedge. Surely they were in range now? Were the boys asleep? Then the skein flared as four reports rang out in rapid succession and from somewhere near the middle of that scattered mob, a large shape fell earthwards. The hedge suddenly disgorged a figure, which ran hell-for-leather out across the field to where the goose had fallen. It was Tom, in a hurry to retrieve his very first goose. Alec had somehow managed to miss, which was not like him and so had Tom with the first shot, but with the second he had pulled out a gander right in front as it tried to back-pedal with wildly flailing wings.

After another hour's wait it was obvious that, for today at least, Uncle Edgar's meadows would only be grazed by his stock. We made our way up the slope towards the car with Tom triumphantly bearing his prize and hardly daring to take his eyes off it in case it shrank or deteriorated in some way before he got it home. We called in on George who congratulated his nephew on his success, promising to make sure Edgar knew who bore the title 'Goose Hunter of the County'. On the strength of that morning's performance, Tom was allowed to take several more mornings after the geese before the season was out, and I understand he put two or three more into the bag. We left my goose with George to give to Edgar as a gesture of thanks for our morning's sport.

10

October 14

A substantial amount of rain fell during the week following our morning after Uncle Edgar's geese, but by the weekend the low clouds thinned somewhat and brighter weather appeared. This coincided with Alec's arrival, and he was not slow to claim some unwarranted credit for the pathetic patch of blue sky that struggled to stay visible even as we watched.

It was mid-day on Saturday and I had arranged with Jack, a farming friend, for us to spend the afternoon taking a quiet walk round his land. My young dog Jet was excited at being included, but I knew that I would have to keep a close eye on him otherwise he would clear a field almost before we set foot in it. The four or five mile drive to the farm was uneventful; in fact we saw only one other vehicle on the road. The flat fields were bordered by ditches that were dry except perhaps for a few puddles of the recent rain water lingering in the lowest parts of the bottom The tall phragmites reeds growing thickly in most of the ditches served as a reminder of the natural environment hereabouts before the fens were drained. In that watery world, thousands

51

of acres of reeds covered much of the swampy land. Some would have been harvested by the fen dwellers either for their own roofs, or for sale to their upland neighbours.

This afternoon we found that the corn had all been harvested, and some stubbles had already been ploughed in. A few fields of potatoes remained awaiting the picker, but the majority of the unharvested fields were of sugar beet, and even some of these had already been prepared to admit the harvester. This was done by digging out roughly twenty rows square from the corners of the fields. The lifted beet was topped by hand and heaped; ready to become part of the first trailer-load.

The fields stretched to the far horizon, the few trees in the scene were dotted around the isolated farmhouses. They were deliberately planted to serve as windbreaks, particularly against winds from an easterly quarter. The black peat soil was deemed far too valuable to allow trees or hedges to take up space anywhere else. In one direction the horizon seemed not so very far away, formed as it was by the bank of a small river, which ran parallel to the road we were driving along, but a mile to our right. After a few minutes the road turned and before long we had come up to the riverbank where a pumping station stood. Water running off the land into the main drain on our side of the bank was pumped by way of culverts through the bank into the river, where it was eventually pumped again, this time out to sea. A windmill had stood in the very same spot a century ago, I told Alec. It was doing the same job, but relying on the inconsistent moods of the wind. There had been 150 of these mills in that small district. Today there are fewer pumping stations because the dependable diesel or electric-powered pumps are umpteen times more efficient and they keep the feet of the fenmen dry for the greater part of the time.

We drove a little way along the base of the bank until the road rose up to a bridge spanning the narrow waterway. I took a quick look as we crossed over. The slow moving surface was barely stirred by a ripple caused by a pair of swans feeding among the rushes along one edge. We passed from the bridge and onto a long straight road, which seemed to go on forever. Almost at the end of this road I turned through a gateway onto a stubble field. Parking where I was sure the car would not be in anybody's way, I let Jet out and made him sit to one side while we sorted out guns and bags. Though he could hardly contain his excitement, Jet behaved himself very well.

After a careful scan around with not a pheasant in sight, we moved off across the stubble. Naturally, we were very visible to game as we walked that bare expanse, but the idea was to persuade the birds to run into the cover of root crops. If any did run ahead we didn't see them, and at the end of the field we carried on over another, larger stubble. Here a covey of partridges flushed well ahead of us, wilder now than those September birds. A potato field was next. The crop was almost harvested, but about thirty rows remained. There were some decent sized spuds lying around among the small stuff left by the harvester. They would only lie there and rot so we gathered some into a pile to pick up later. We walked either side of the rows but the only bird in there, a hen pheasant, ran ahead of us until she reached the end of the field whereupon she took wing and skimmed away over a field of beet.

Alec and I entered that beet some five minutes later and spread forty yards apart to walk through it. The crop was of the sort that reaches one's thighs and is hard work to push through, but we were still young enough then to think nothing of covering thirty or forty acres of the stuff during an afternoon. Nevertheless, it was not long before we were both pretty warm. It was too hot for leggings so black seeds spilled into our boots and even beet leaves found their way down there. Later on, especially when it was wet, I would be wearing an old pair of thigh boots. For the moment we ploughed onwards, red in the face and hot under the collar. Whirrr! A hen bird got up from behind and took us both by surprise. We had been pushing on and on without sign of game and not even the dog showing much interest, until we had reached that almost trance-like state as if automatic pilot has cut in and concentration wanes. I turned and took a wild shot at the departing pheasant, but missed by a mile. Concentrating now, we walked on steadily until we neared the last forty yards of the field. We were seriously on the alert now for if anything is going to flush it is often at the end of cover, where there is nowhere else to run. Jet was ahead now nose down, tail wagging. Yes... he's definitely onto something. I give a warning to Alec. Jet is off, surging ahead. It doesn't matter because we are at the field's end. Up jumps a hen pheasant and up swings Alec's gun, only to be lowered again as the hen is followed by eight or nine half-grown poults, squeaking in her wake.

We turn, move another fifty yards over and walk back down the field, repeating this until we have covered the whole twenty acres. On the last walk through, after flushing yet another brood too young even to raise a gun at, we began to think there were no mature birds around - that we should practice what we preach and not even think of pheasant shooting until November. Then, suddenly everything changes and there is a wild clatter as we blunder into half a dozen pheasants. Seeming to burst out of the ground from the same spot they departed to every point of the compass. A big old cock bird was rising fast and crowing his challenge to the world, all red and gold against the sky and his tail quivering with effort. My shot took him at the peak of his climb and he fell over backwards to crash into the cover. Alec had two hens down and Jet was already bringing one in. He had been ranging over to my right and had not winded the birds we had flushed. This was more like it, but then we always knew we would find some shootable pheasants in October. Of course we did!

From the beet we walked a reedy dyke for half a mile before Alec killed a cock, which had tried to make a dash for it. Making our way back along another dyke-side we could see that it would bring us to yet another potato field. We pressed on hopefully. One hundred yards from the potatoes Jet, who had been the perfect gundog all of the afternoon, got onto a scent and switched into 'selective hearing' mode. For all my shouts, threats and curses he went along that dyke-side like the London to Edinburgh express. Bearing safety in mind we moved as fast as we could, in time to see the dog charge into the potatoes and begin weaving about as the pheasant he was on did its best to evade him. Then a flurry of wings as three birds rose. We slumped to a halt, the race lost, but no, one of the birds, a cock, had swung back our way. Anyone who thinks that wild fen pheasants cannot fly should have seen this fellow. After one hundred yards he was already over thirty yards up and still climbing. He came past Alec well out and going like a rocket. Alec swung up and slew him with a spectacular shot. I took a step towards him with thoughts of congratulations and almost trod on a hen that had been skulking there the whole time. I added her to the bag with an easy shot. Eventually, Jet came back and much to his disappointment I put him on the lead.

The walk took us back over another stubble field where an old hare slipped from her form. It would have been a simple shot, but she was in luck, as neither of us wanted a hare. We made a slight detour to collect our gleaned potatoes before ambling back to the car. As we had three cock-and-hen brace I stopped at the farmhouse to drop off a brace for my friend Jack and his wife Sally. In fact it was Sally who came to the door. Jack was seeing to his horses she said, but he would be pleased to know that we had enjoyed some sport.

As we drove home Alec told me of a friend of his called Ernie. Ernie was about fourteen years old and was keen to take up shooting. Although he had no gun, would wander through the countryside learning the ways of the birds and animals. One day he was loitering near a smallholding, with no particular plans in mind, when he spotted the farmer approaching on his bicycle. Ernie, taking no chances, went and hid in a nearby ditch. The farmer had a small stack of straw on one of his fields, and he proceeded to lean his velocipede against it. As Ernie watched from his hiding place, the farmer fumbled in the stack and to the young onlooker's astonishment withdrew a twelve-bore shotgun. Taking a couple of cartridges from his pocket he loaded the gun and stalked off into his potatoes in search of game. History does not relate whether not a shot was fired or game was bagged - what mattered was that at the end of his walk the smallholder replaced his gun in the stack and cycled off home. Now Ernie had a gun! Whenever he could cadge ammunition from older friends he would hurry down to the stack and 'borrow' the gun for a walk round somebody's roots. Alec thought that this wheeze lasted either for as long as the stack was there, or until the youth was old enough to purchase his own weapon.

We had eaten early and put our feet up for an hour, but although we had been healthily tired after our pheasant shooting I felt that there was still something left of the day.

"Do you fancy trying for a duck?" I enquired of my friend. "We can be down the wash in a quarter of an hour."

As expected, Alec confirmed that he was game for any sport in the offing so we were not long in heading out to the car. It was not *The* Wash that was our destination, but local fresh marshes known as washlands because of the way the winter floodwater is allowed to wash over them. After we had selected suitable cartridges and kit, it was a little over the predicted fifteen minutes by the time we arrived and began bumping down a far from level gravel drove. We crossed a bridge over a narrow waterway and parked the car just beyond it. Jet sprang joyfully out and bounded about until we struck off along a continuation of the drove. The drove curved round between marshes which were grazed by sturdy, sleek looking bullocks. Through a five-barred gate we went, and as is usual with this type of gate, unless they are brand new, we had to lift the gate to allow it to open and close properly. Once through, we were walking along a straight reach of the drove. On either side of the track, the water in the dykes was brimming to the edges and showing through the thick growth of rushes.

The sun was sinking as we hurried on past four or five field gates, before we came to the marsh I had selected for the evening. Walking across to the cover of a nearby dyke we found that we were splashing through shallow water. If one looked down the water could be seen gleaming among the grasses and the short rushes cropped by recently grazing cattle.

"This is a bonus," I said, looking at Alec.

"I wonder whether the duck have found it yet? There's bound to be seeds floating about in here." I left my friend hiding among tall grasses while I moved on a hundred yards or so to where a railway sleeper fence post stood leaning at a

57

crazy angle. I knelt at the base of the sleeper and watched the western sky as the pale greys and apple greens blended with soft pink behind a distant hedge, every twig of which was etched black before the light.

A heron beat slowly across the washland until he reached the big river on the far side. He gave a harsh cry that echoed and re-echoed from the banks and then he set his wide wings to glide down for a spot of night fishing. A party of lapwings whirled by in a tumbling mass of noisy blurred shapes. Snipe began to drop in, their distinctive calls heralding their approach. It made no difference; I still could not spot them. A rush of wings and they were down, at times pitching in very closely. Finally, I saw one clearly silhouetted against the water within ten feet of me. Surely I would see that if I flushed it? The answer was supplied for me because I must have made a slight movement and the snipe jumped. I never saw it, it would have sped quickly away, low and invisible in the gloom. Kekkekkekek! Six, eight, nine mallard swinging in over the next field.

I could see them clearly enough even though they were still well out of shot. They swept across and seemed to turn towards me, but were lost to sight in a darkening patch of sky. Anxious moments followed during which I knelt, lips slightly apart, listening intently. Then came the hiss and whistle of pinions as the duck passed unseen overhead. Moments later the sound of steadily beating pinions again, fainter this time, fainter still… boom! I think the sudden report startled me as much as the unsuspecting duck.

The light had gone now so I splashed my way to where Alec was hiding to find him standing there waiting for me.

"Missed 'em!" Alec pre-empted my question. "They were well up, but they came nicely and I ought to have had one."

When we returned to the drove we walked for about a quarter of a mile before we became aware of something in front of us. It soon became obvious that some bullocks had escaped from a field, but luckily the drove gate was shut, preventing them from wandering any further. I slipped the lead over Jet's head - we had to get through the herd and cattle tend to get a bit silly when a dog is near them at night. There was not a lot of room, but we managed to squeeze past the side of the heaving, steaming mass until we could turn them back the way they had come. I like cattle. I even like the smell of them, childhood memories I suppose, but I had not fancied one of their hooves coming down on my rubber-shod foot. We arrived back home to find that my wife had thoughtfully decorated the kitchen table with a wedge of mature cheddar cheese along with a very large jar of pickled onions and to accompany this fine fare, a couple of bottles of Guinness. We enjoyed our late supper as we went over the day, shot by shot, and even Jet was forgiven for his lapse of self-control.

11

October 15

When the alarm clock shattered the early morning silence I was still dead to the world, which is very rare. There's normally no need for an alarm because my body clock will ensure that I am awake at least half-an-hour before the time I need to be up and dressed. The exertions of yesterday had obviously affected Alec as well for when I tapped on his door the muffled sounds of his rousing came to the ear. I smiled the smug smile of one who is first up and hurried quietly down the stairs to get a pot of coffee on the go. My intention was to test his patience by claiming to have been up a good thirty minutes. When Alec did come down he quietly sipped his coffee and with years of exchanging banter behind him, wisely refused to rise to the bait.

His first real conversation of the morning was to welcome the fact that there was quite a strong wind blowing. As it was Sunday, it was to the marshes of the more liberal minded county of Lincolnshire that we were bound on this particular morning. As was often the case on a Sunday we did not see one other vehicle during the whole journey across the lonely fens. Of course, the roads we traversed were far from major; on the contrary most of them would not even merit the designation of B road. There were very few signposts and a stranger would soon be lost on the routes we took, but we were on our own patch and completely at home. In later years a Londoner would talk to me about the fens. He had recently moved to an isolated village near Spalding. I asked him how he had settled in.

"Oh, I love it," he replied. "It's the only place in England where I could lay across the middle of the road for half an hour and not be run over!"

Eventually we passed a public house with a pond in its grounds. The pond was full of mallard, but they were tame birds probably reared by the publican. One young friend who sometimes accompanied us to the marsh always begged us to stop there and give them a couple of barrels. Needless to say, we steadfastly turned a deaf ear to his pleadings. Not long after that we drove through a village until the road climbed abruptly up the bank of a muddy-channelled tidal river. Following the river along for two or three miles we crossed it by means of a well-known swing bridge. Once on the other side we continued following the river until the road in front was barred by a gate, beyond which loomed the vague shape of a low lighthouse. The trees that formed an avenue lining the driveway up to the East Lighthouse were being buffeted by the wind. The only downside to this otherwise welcome sight was the fact that it was the prevailing south-westerly and so off the land, in other words, right up the tail of any duck flying into the marsh at dawn. Yes, that same wind would be in the face of geese flighting off the sands, but this early in the season we were not really expecting to see pinkfeet. The few that had arrived so far would likely be north of the river at Gedney Drove End or Shep White's.

61

Ever optimistic we tumbled out of the car, which I had parked on the bank just off the road and set off along the bank under the lee of the lighthouse. It was here, in the 1930's that Peter Scott set up home as a base for his wildfowling activities, and as a studio where he produced many of his famous paintings. It was here too that Scott started the collection of wildfowl, which after the Second World War became the nucleus of the larger collection he built up on founding the Wildfowl Trust. Whenever I passed the lighthouse I could not help imagining Peter Scott a quarter of a century before, either at his easel or setting off in his punt out into the estuary. No lights showed from the tower this morning and we pressed on at a good pace eager to cover the distance between it and the point where the seawall turned. Beyond that point was the wild expanse of saltings and mud that we cherished.

At last we made the bend and descended to the track at the base of the landward side of the sea bank. Once on the track we pressed on for about half a mile before climbing the bank to go over onto the marsh. The tide had covered half of the saltings and had ebbed as far as the stalk edges, so creeks still had to be jumped with care. As we splashed through the wet grasses so recently left by the sea, beads of phosphorescence showered from our boots like sparks from a grinder.

"We must look like the devil's horsemen!" Alec muttered.

We then came to a creek that was too wide to jump, forcing us to wait until the tide ebbed a bit more. The water was fairly rushing out, but even so we cast anxious glances at the eastern horizon, imagining it was getting lighter, even as we watched. In the end our patience was exhausted and Alec slipped down the side of the creek and just made it across. I followed and must have stepped into a slightly

deeper place for I felt the cold water enter one of my boots. "
I cursed bitterly as Alec, grinning like a Cheshire cat, held
out his hand to pull me up.

"Could have been January," He reasoned, laughing at my
plight.

He was right of course, and I knew from the experience of
many a full boot, that the water would soon take on the
temperature of my foot.

Now we would go our separate ways to find a place to hide
before the light came. I struck off to the right and found
some taller grass near a small creek. I say taller grass, by
which I mean tall enough to give the barest cover to a
kneeling man. In the half-light, provided one keeps still, it is
ample. I knelt facing the mainland and waited for the new
day to dawn. If I looked back over my shoulder, the street
lamps of faraway Hunstanton showed as pinpricks of light.
To the left front, a faint glow reflected from the low clouds
indicated the presence of King's Lynn. As the eastern sky
became a lighter grey the little world around me began to
wake up. A curlew called mournfully from out on the mud
where the tide had by now uncovered his breakfast. Marshes
without the curlew would just not feel right, this bird is so
very much part of the scene. As a shelduck's laughing call
echoed over the flats, it reminded me of a friend whose stock
comment was. "They are laughing at us silly buggers who
have left a warm bed *and* an even warmer missus to come
and squat out here. They are right, we must be bloody mad!"

There came the rush of very small wings as an unseen
dunlin or stint passed close by. Occasionally, the strange
moan of a seal came to the ears. The smell of the mud and
rank vegetation also made it's own contribution to that quiet
time of waiting. A very soft hiss of wings made me turn but
it was only the first wave of gulls flying in, a long line of

63

them, almost silent. Another line followed and another beyond them. If only the duck would fly so low. The last birds of the third wave came over me and flared as I looked up at them and they spotted my white face. Then they were gone and I was alone once more.

There appeared a band of angry red under the clouds as the sky lightened. I heared, rather than saw the first duck pass over. The next lot I did see, a dozen black shapes wings almost a blur, but they were so high I did not even grip the gun. I turned to watch as they flew out beyond the saltings and began a leisurely descent, which would bring them to rest far out on the sandbanks. Even as I watched my eyes caught sight of a movement below the duck - a wavering line of birds just above the mud. No! Are they? Then a faint "wink! wink!" reached my ear. They were pinkfooted geese all right. I slithered down into the now waterless creek and watched them. They were nearer now. I could see that there were twenty in the skein but I could also see that, as is usual along this coast, they were moving to the left. They would even pass well wide of Alec, who I knew was somewhere five hundred yards to my left. The geese climbed rapidly before they reached the saltings and headed in the direction of the lighthouse. When they were past, the sound of their music was brought back to us on the wind. What lovely music it is and in itself, worth the effort of turning out this morning.

Spots of rain began to fall as if to confirm the warning of that earlier red sky and I faced the land again, in time to see yet another team of mallard streaming out to their daytime sanctuary. Then the bump of a shot caused me to look in Alec's direction. His figure suddenly emerged from the mud and I watched him plod across the marsh, stoop and pick up something, which was deposited in his side-bag. He settled again and disappears from view. After another half an hour it was fully light and the rain was coming down in earnest. With not much prospect of any further duck I struggled to my feet and began the soggy walk back the seawall. My wet foot seemed hardly relevant now. I could see Alec making his way back and fifteen minutes later our paths converged

"What did you get?" I enquired.

"A wigeon." came the reply. "I had just turned to watch some mallard when a little gang of them came from behind me. They were only a few yards above the mud."

Once on the seawall we quickly made progress and though the rain did its best to dampen our spirits we were in fact pretty warm by the time we reached the car. Most of the homeward journey was spent trying to keep the windscreen clear of the condensation we were generating.

12

October 20

Whilst we were driving home from the marsh last weekend Alec had mentioned in passing that George's nephew, young Tom, who had spent plenty of time shooting inland, always seemed to be interested in hearing about our coastal wildfowling experiences. He had recently expressed a desire to try it for himself one day. It had set me thinking until in the end I had telephoned Alec with the suggestion that we invite the lad to join us occasionally. In fact if Alec was not opposed to the idea, why didn't he bring him along on Friday evening - we had plenty of room at the house and he would be more than welcome. Alec agreed and said he would put it to Tom the very next day. Thus it turned out that the pair of them pitched up as arranged. As it was too late to go out that evening, we relaxed with a beer while Tom regaled us with the story of his latest walk round his uncle's farm. He had put up a cock pheasant, which had flown in the general direction of a rough gravel-based hollow that had been used as the farm rubbish tip. Among the broken crates and sheets of corrugated iron was a sizable area of rough grass riddled with rabbit runs and burrows - just the sort of place that would attract a crafty old cock. Tom made his way there and walked, he thought, every inch of the hollow without a sign of the pheasant. He assumed that his bird had after all not chosen to pitch there, so had made to leave. For some reason he took a last glance back over his shoulder and there was the pheasant, running neck outstretched and low around a clump of grass. If the old codger had stayed put for a few moments more he would never have been spotted. As it was Tom dodged quickly up to a slight rise in the ground where the cock would come into view. The quick reaction worked because the long-tail, realising that the game was up, was forced to fly but as Tom now recalled, he didn't fly very far.

Refilling our glasses, I explained to Tom how the washlands in the fens protect a huge acreage of arable land by serving as great holding areas for floodwater. Massive banks confine the floodwaters until they can be released, via sluice gates, into the river systems on an ebbing tide. Tom learned that the cattle marshes that are the washlands provide habitat for a variety of wildlife. But none more spectacular than the dramatic hordes of wintering wildfowl, which in turn have resulted in a centuries-old tradition of wildfowling, which goes on to this day.

I went on to relate an amusing anecdote told to me by a friend and fellow wildfowler. Stan was a carpenter by trade, and after one particular job found himself with a quantity of 2"x 4" timber off-cuts left over from the work. Rather than dispose of them, Stan and his friend Russ decided to make use of the wood by turning the blocks into wigeon decoys. They cut out the basic shapes with saw and hand axe before carving them roughly to represent the wild duck they intended to attract. The decoys were painted with white flanks and conspicuous white shoulders. Ring eyes were screwed in to take the weighted lines and all was ready.

It was decided to try out the decoys on the floods at Welche's Dam on the Hundred Foot Washes. So after lashing their punt to the roof rack of Stan's van, the pair set off early one Saturday morning. The washes were flooded to a depth of about two feet and they lost time in launching and setting off before the dawn. After paddling for some time they came across a particularly reedy dyke, where they steered into the thick cover. Having selected their hiding place the young men set out their brand new, untried decoys forty yards from the reeds and then paddled back into cover to wait.

With dawn came the sun, which lit up the surroundings. They saw a few duck, but none offered them a chance so by 11 o'clock they decided to break for a bite to eat. Paddling to a piece of higher ground they beached the punt and sat in it to eat their lunch. Although they were some way off, the decoys were still well in view, causing Russ to comment that from this range they looked even more realistic. Just then two heads appeared over the riverbank only to hastily disappear again. A few minutes later two youths came belly crawling over the bank pulling a boat behind them. From their cover Stan and Russ watched with interest.

"They've seen our decoys," said Stan. "I reckon they're going to shoot at them - they think they're real ducks!"

The boys pushed their boat into the flood and crept slowly forward, fondly imagining their clumsy manoeuvres to be invisible to the little party of wildfowl, which still swam in front of that reedy dyke. On arriving at a point they considered to be within range up they got and loosed off two barrels. Nothing flew of course and there was a pregnant pause after which the words - "They're flipping decoys!"

came drifting across the water. Stan and Russ could hardly stop themselves from laughing out loud as the boys looked sheepishly around before beating a hasty retreat. They would never know that hidden spectators had greatly enjoyed their antics.

Stan and Russ resumed their lunch during which a mallard carelessly flew near enough for Russ to bring it to the bag. That was their only chance and as it was almost noon, the duo decided to gather up the decoys and call it a day. On close inspection they discovered that not one of the boys pellets had struck the wooden ducks. Stan had laughed when telling me the tale and had said.

"I don't think they could have had any shot in their cartridges. Those decoys never did outwit many ducks, but they certainly fooled them ol' boys that day."

This little story prompted others in a similar vein - decoys that were shot at and hit, birds thought to be decoys then suddenly sprouted wings, got up and flew off and decoys that fooled raptors. An example of the latter came when I had set out twenty or thirty pigeon decoys on a newly drilled field of mustard. Squatting in a netting hide within forty yards of the artificial birds, I had enjoyed some good shooting early on, but the steady trickle of birds had dried up to be replaced by a long quiet period. I sat contemplating the scene before the hide and had begun to consider packing up. I told myself to give it fifteen minutes more. That thought was drifting across my mind when a blurred grey shape whizzed in from the left causing me to grip the gun. This was no woodpigeon though, but a peregrine falcon bent on snatching an easy meal. The falcon must have expected this flock of feeding pigeon to scatter at her approach - but they didn't. She swept up in a vertical climb, looped the loop and came back for a second look at these rather brave or very stupid pigeons. On this flypast it must have sunk in that all was not what it seemed, and the peregrine banked before darting off for good.

Another class of predator was convinced that a decoy was the real thing when I decided to have a bit of fun with our cats, who for the purposes of this story I will call Tig and Tag. While they were dozing in the kitchen I set up a solid woodpigeon decoy on the lawn, with its back to the house. Then I carried Tig to the window and made sure he had seen the decoy, but he didn't seem interested. I fetched Tag and got an instant reaction - his mouth opened and twitched. I opened the door and slipped Tag out while I watched through the window. Tag crouched and began a snake-like stalk across the lawn. Now Tig was interested and bounded over Tag in an all out race for the prey. Tag, realising that further stealth was useless, also charged. Both cats hit the decoy at the same moment, bowling it over and ending up in a heap with it. The two felines stood up in an attempt to regain their natural dignity, but what they could not disguise were the expressions of total disbelief and confusion that remained on their faces for several seconds. Meanwhile I was shaking with laughter at their antics.

Some more good yarns were exchanged until there came a moment when the stories dried up and glasses were drained. It was a moment I think when we all realised simultaneously that if we were to rise in good time in the morning, we had better think about climbing the old wooden hill.

Having risen well before time I was surprised to hear movements in the kitchen as I crept downstairs the next morning. It was Tom.

"I've been awake for hours," he said, immediately bringing back memories of my youth. I used to get so excited by the prospect of sport and half afraid that I would not hear the alarm clock, or worse still that the alarm clock might not go off at all, that sleep was all but impossible. I would restlessly toss and turn as the church clock chimed away each hour, and then if one did drop off fitfully it was only to wake an hour or so before the alarm was due. I would lie there as tense as a coiled spring waiting in the darkness for its sudden summons. And then after all that state of preparedness, didn't it always make me jump when it rang at last! To Tom I simply replied. "Yes. I know just what you mean old son." Alec soon joined us and we all went out to the car. While the others piled in the guns and bags, I opened the kennel door to let out Jet, who bounded across the gravel to take a flying leap into the back of the car, ensuring that there was space for him to curl up amongst our gear. Finally, I hurried back into the house to take my wife a reconciliatory cup of tea and then we were on our way.

Forty minutes later we drew the car to a halt right under the sea wall, and set about pulling on our boots. Tom, I noticed had knee boots covered with over-trousers, we would have to be careful where we took him. The tide was now in and had already begun to ebb, but it would be a while before those short boots would be of use. We decided to wait hidden, by the sea wall at first, in the vain hope that a foolhardy duck might fly in low. In short order a wedge of five mallard did come right over us, chuckling to each other as they sped seawards. We gave no thought to raising the gun, as they were two gunshots high at the very least. Then miraculously, a duck did fly low over the bank and Tom's gun was up in an instant.

"Whoa!" Alec and I cried as one voice. Tom held his fire and the shelduck flew on unscathed. We explained the differences between shelduck and legitimate quarry species, whilst, at the same time giving the lad other useful tips for identification. We told him that the flock patterns of parties, even when the birds appear as mere dots in the sky, would always be recognised as duck by an experienced wildfowler.

There are other guidelines of course. For example, we know that wigeon often fly in large companies, speeding in arc formations high in the sky. On the other hand, after the early season stubble feeding flocks, it is more usual to see mallard at flight time, travelling in smaller teams.

We went on to point out to Tom that in the dark or in poor light, the wing beats of individual duck are useful for identification purposes. The shelduck for instance, has slow, whistling beats, which readily give it away, even in the dark. Then there are diving duck, like tufted or pochard. These have short wings that beat so fast, the sound they make is a continuous rushing hiss, which is audible some time before the party of fowl pass by. And, if the birds are calling, well that is a bonus. Even the newcomer to the sport will not be long before he begins to recognise the various whistles, quacks, growls and grunts that make up the vocabulary of our native wild duck. We decided that we had passed on enough information for the time being and we had better concentrate on the job in hand.

The tide had retreated enough to allow us access to the saltings, but Tom was still restricted when creeks or gutters that barred his way were too wide for him to jump over. By the time it was getting light we were about halfway out towards the stalk edges, so we knelt down where we were, amongst patches of spartina, facing the land and any incoming duck. There was not enough wind to be overly optimistic and most of the birds we saw flew well out of range. This however, was not terribly important on this day because we were able to show Tom how the fowl flew in at dawn, and he could see first-hand just why strong onshore winds were important. One lone mallard came lower and was possibly in shot had it been overhead, but it flew slap-bang between us, when we were separated by one hundred and forty yards of saltmarsh, so that possibility was to remain academic. Alec pointed out to our apprentice that as geese roosted out on the sandbanks, where they ingested sand as grit to aid digestion, when they flew in at first light it was an offshore wind that was desired by the wildfowler crouching in muddy ambush.

A small company of wigeon came tearing along the erratic margin where marsh meets bare mud. There came a whistle or two, but they were mostly silent. We were forced to watch impotently from a distance as the group passed, only feet above the mud, and the white of their bellies strikingly obvious. The water level in the gutters had receded enough to allow further outward progress, but it wasn't long before Tom's Wellington boots were filled. I suppose he had been lucky to remain dry shod for so long. We assured him that if he took up the sport of wildfowling this would not be the last time he went home with wet feet - even thigh boots succumbed occasionally. Having said that, we strongly advised him to purchase a pair of thigh boots as soon as possible, preferably a brand like Hood 'Bull's-eye', as they are made with slightly thicker rubber and are more resistant to damage from unfortunate contact with barbed wire. Unlike some of the lighter, angling waders, they also stand up on their own without the necessity of those additional straps attaching them to one's belt to keep them up.

We stationed Tom in a deep creek hoping that, although most of the curlew had returned to the out marsh to feed, we might be lucky enough to get Tom a shot at a latecomer. Eventually a curlew appeared and it was coming in our direction. Out of the corner of my eye I saw Alec slowly sink down out of sight. He was some distance away along our creek, but he was taking no chances.

"Keep the bird in sight, but watch him from under the peak of your cap." I whispered to Tom. "As he comes on, you will be able to crouch lower. Wait until he is right overhead." I got right down and watched the youth. He did everything right, but when it came to the shot he fell into the trap that ensnares many a newcomer - he misjudged the speed of the bird. Curlew always seem to be flying slowly and appear to be an easy target, impossible to miss, when they are of course, nothing of the sort. Young Tom put up his gun and poked, which resulted in the inevitable miss with both barrels. He watched the bird fly on, screeching blue murder, with an incredulous expression on his face that clearly conveyed the question, 'How *did* I miss that?'

On the way back to the sea wall we explained to the youngster the amount of salting that he should expect to be covered by tide at each phase of the moon, from the neaps which scarcely invade the marsh, to the springs which reach right up to the sea wall and at times put it severely to the test. We explained how strong winds could radically affect the height and time of the tide. Finally, it was suggested that a good maxim was - When going out to shoot on a rising tide, never cross a creek that you cannot jump. Considering that Tom had had enough to absorb for one day, we did not push any more information or marsh lore onto him. Instead we left him to savour the scene and take in the atmosphere of this wild place. On regaining the sea wall the youngster sat down to remove his boots and expressed surprise at how little water there was inside.

"I thought there would be a couple of gallons in each one," he said, with a wry grin. We waited, showering the lad with gentle banter, until he had wrung out his socks and tried to put them back on while wet. In the end he gave up, thrust his bare feet back into his boots and squelched his way back along the grassy track at the base of the sea bank. We could see though, that it was his feet and not his spirit that felt dampened, and we knew that he already had the makings of a wildfowler.

13

October 28

The wind was literally howling through the trees around Alec's cottage and in truth, if some of them had been uprooted before my eyes I would not have been surprised. As I swung the car into the yard, the headlights picked up a spiralling stream of leaves that came rushing horizontally towards me like so many oversized brown snowflakes. Taking care not to allow the car door to be ripped out of my hand, I stumbled towards the back entrance of the cottage. The door opened very slightly so that just a chink of yellow light shone through. I was almost on the threshold, before Alec opened up just wide enough to allow me to dodge past him, whereupon he slammed the door shut.

"Sorry about that," he said. "But with the wind in this direction we would have soon had a kitchen full of leaves to sweep up."

"Yes, and it wouldn't have been me doing the sweeping!" Molly added, with a smile. We sat down to roast gadwall and not for the first time agreed that the gadwall must have the whitest meat of all the duck tribe. It was quite some time after supper, as the three of us were sitting at the scrubbed pine kitchen table chatting away, when Alec paused and looked up.

"I've got a bit of a surprise lined up for you tomorrow morning. I hadn't said anything before because I wasn't even sure myself. Anyway, now that I've had the date confirmed I can tell you - We've got an invitation to a morning flight on the old Colonel's private Broad!"

"Phew! How the devil did you wangle that?" I asked incredulously.

"Oh, there's nothing mysterious about it," Alec replied. "The old boy had promised me a morning last season in return for a bit of business I was able to put his way. It was just a matter of him being able to fit me into his schedule, he might be retired, but he still leads a pretty busy life. Anyway, we'll have to be up in good time tomorrow as his place is about ten miles the other side of Norwich."

The wind had slackened somewhat during the night, but it was still rattling the sash windows in their frames when I roused in the early hours of the next morning. I heard Alec's futile attempt to quietly creak his way down the stairs, so I scrambled into my clothes and made my own way down to the smell of hot coffee emanating from the kitchen doorway. My friend had turned the tables on me after last weekend.

"Some folk do have trouble getting up in the morning," he mumbled without bothering to look up. He was busy chewing on a bacon sandwich in which I swear that there was as much mustard as there was meat. I asked if he had bought shares in the famous local mustard company.

"Yew carn't beat it bor!" Alec exclaimed, replying in the vernacular. He grinned as he continued masticating with obvious relish, undeterred by any scurrilous comment of mine. Seeing he was not going to respond to any mischief, I brought the conversation to the matter before us.

"Are there any special considerations for this morning?"

Alec wiped a crumb from his mouth.

"Oh, it will only be us and the Colonel, so your ordinary marsh clothes will be all right... in fact they'd be best really if it rains. You won't need your magnum though, just take your game gun and a bag of cartridges. I'm taking number six shot, with a few fours in case of higher stuff."

We collected these items from Alec's den, or perhaps I should say study, and drove off in the old Ford Popular along some dark Norfolk roads for what seemed like an age. At last we came to a junction with a main trunk road, and once we had turned on to that the miles were soon eaten up. I suppose it was about half an hour later that we had left the trunk road and were back once again on hedged-in narrow lanes. Hares and rabbits ran, momentarily caught in the searching beam of the headlights. They ran along ahead of us before taking the brave leap through the beam into what must have appeared to them as a frightening pitch-black void. We travelled through some pines, which seemed to close in on us making the lane even narrower. I hadn't a clue where we were, but suddenly Alec turned off through a gap in the trees. The manoeuvre was so abrupt that there was more than a suspicion that he had almost missed the turn, but I held my tongue. The car was now bumping along a grass track, gravelled only where the wheels of a vehicle might run. We continued this switchback ride until we crunched to a halt in front of an old house with tall gables and ornamented Victorian chimney pots. A lamp burned in a downstairs room and even as Alec switched off the engine someone opened a door, allowing a shaft of light to spill out onto, what we could now see was, a flagged yard. In the gloom the place had a rather sinister atmosphere and I thought that it would not have looked out of place as an illustration in a Sherlock Holmes novel. Thankfully, there was nothing at all sinister about the character who emerged from the door, beaming a silent greeting as he strode over to the car.

"I say, what a splendid morning you've brought with you," he boomed. "If only this wind holds we might have some fun."

As the unrelenting wind lashing the trees was, I recalled, due to the autumn equinox, I for one, had no reason to believe that it would ease significantly during the next few hours. We left the warmth of the car and Alec introduced me to the Colonel. After shaking hands our host was impatient to make a start.

"We'd best get on, I don't have to tell you wildfowler fellows that we need to be in position before light."

He waved us over to an ancient petrol Land Rover, in which a couple of excited spaniels could be seen. I hadn't spotted the vehicle before as it was parked in a dark corner of the yard. Once we had fought for and won a seat from the dogs, the Colonel shoved the vehicle into gear and drove us further along the track at the rear of the house. After we had chugged along for a few minutes we were clear of the trees and crossing open ground. The track joined a concrete road, which we drove along until we passed a straw stack and came upon a tall, thick hawthorn hedge. Here, the Colonel drew up and parked. We disembarked in the wake of the dogs, which had clambered over us upon sighting the slightest of gaps in the opening door. Oblivious to the bellows of their master they tore around in wild excitement, until we were out of the Land Rover with our guns. Incredibly, in view of the previous few seconds, they became calmer immediately and appeared ready for whatever job their master had in mind.

They trotted at the Colonel's heels as that gentleman led the way through a gate in the hedge. Once beyond the gate we entered an area of tall reeds through which paths of some eight feet wide had been cut, presumably by an Allen scythe or some similar implement. We followed our host along one of these paths until it suddenly curved to the left. As soon as we rounded the bend we noticed that the track ended at a boarded walkway with stout posts and rails. We thumped along the boards and I realised that we were over water. This must be the edge of the broad and the boardwalk was like a small pier taking us out beyond the reed fringe. At the end of the pier, which was no more than fifteen to twenty feet long, there was another section at right angles forming the top of a capital T. This had been constructed to create a butt for two guns, standing some ten feet apart at either end and covering two different bays. The rails round the butt sandwiched a filling of reeds at least three inches thick, possibly more. I could well imagine that from the other side it would be undistinguishable from the rest of the reed shoal. It was a clever idea for a smaller-sized lake or pond where safety angles are more of a problem than they would be on a larger expanse of water. Even in the darkness, I could see that it was very well put together on its supporting piles. The Colonel's voice broke in on my observations.

"I'll leave it to you to sort out an end each - I'm going to a butt to the right of you. Don't worry we won't be in each other's line of fire...Oh! And the dogs will pick up - that is assuming that you can hit 'em!" Still chuckling he disappeared into the fastness of his fen.

Left to our own devices Alec and I took up our respective positions at each end of the butt. I dipped into the cartridge bag behind me for a handful of fives, which I deposited into the right-hand pocket of my jacket. I looked at the grey sky, which was a touch lighter now. Clouds of a darker shade of grey were being blown rapidly overhead by winds that were obviously of a considerably greater velocity than those that buffeted us. I supposed that on such a morning any self-respecting duck would be glad to find sheltered waters on which to spend the day. But was this water sheltered? I could not tell, not for the moment for it was still too dark to see anything below where the horizon would appear. The sky was definitely lighter though, I hadn't been able to discern that dead tree a few minutes ago and...Straight past that same dead tree and angling in towards me flew a pair of mallard, with the wind in their tails. Slap-bang overhead they came and although there was time for only one shot, the duck folded and crashed in a more than satisfactory fashion. It is always a boost to the confidence to start the day with a successful shot, especially on strange ground. The sound of the report was lost in the wind and almost before I had reloaded three more mallard had appeared. Alec shouted a warning, but I had seen them. This trio were flying into the wind and obviously intending to plane down at any moment. As they crossed in front of us, both guns swung up as one. We both fired and - glory be - all three duck tumbled out of the sky! What a start, four to three shots. But of course, as is the nature of things, we were quickly brought back down to earth by a series of seemingly inexplicable misses. Particularly misses at teal that seemed always to fly into the shadows, just when one was about to squeeze the trigger. And how those little devils could twist and turn and corkscrew in formations that would put the Red Arrows to shame.

Before long it became light enough to see that the area of water was not that big, perhaps less than a couple of acres. Even so, despite the strong winds, there were substantial patches of virtually calm water in the lee of the tall reed shoals, and that was an added attraction on a day like this. I was looking at such a bay to my right when two muffled reports came from the Colonel's gun. Seconds later, twin spurts of water clearly indicated where his birds had fallen. A louder gunshot from my left caused me to turn towards Alec in time to see a team of duck beating a hasty retreat out over the tasselled heads of the reeds. I thought I glimpsed a flash of white speculum, but they did not hang around long enough for me to get a good look. My turn came again when a single duck from the Colonel's direction came belting over my right shoulder. Not my favourite angle for a shot so I turned and swung with it. It came almost as a surprise when the bird's neck flung back and it fell beyond the hedge.

A soft footfall on the boardwalk heralded the return of the Colonel.

"That's it chaps," he called. "We'll call it a day now if you don't mind - I like to let the later lots come in to a quiet haven."

It had been a terrific morning and we told the old boy so. We understood the importance stopping while duck were still coming in and were more than happy for our host to call a halt when he felt fit - after all he knew his water. He walked off at a brisk pace, spaniels at heel and before long we could hear the sounds of picking-up in progress - dogs swimming, splashing through the shallower parts, and crashing through reeds in response to their master's words of encouragement and praise. Could these be the same 'wild' hounds we had met earlier in the day? During this calm after the storm, I was able to take a better look at the broad. I doubted if, in fact, it was a broad in the truest sense - The Broads had been created by the natural flooding of ancient peat diggings and they were generally far larger. More likely this water was a worked out clay or gravel pit, but if the Colonel wanted to call it a broad that was fine by me. I had been feeling guilty about standing idly by, while our host was working his socks off attempting to collect our birds. There was no way that we could help him, of course, and to be fair he hadn't expected it. Nevertheless I felt I must do something, so I walked back along the reed-fenced pathway and out of the gate to look for my last bird, which had fallen beyond the hedge. I hoped fervently that it had indeed cleared the hedge and was not lodged up in that thorny mass. As it was I had no trouble in finding it, a mallard duck lying in full view in the middle of the road. As I was inspecting it, I heard the muffled voices of the others and guessed correctly, that they were making their way to the gate so I waited where I was. Sure enough after a moment or two they appeared at the gate complete with a bulging sack and a pair of bedraggled, but happy looking spaniels. I noted that Alec was carrying the sack, thereby relieving his own feelings of guilt.

Suddenly we all froze and looked skywards for we had all heard them at the same time, wild geese on the wing. Then they appeared, a good five hundred of them - pinkfeet, flying in from Wells to feed on the fields. There were three skeins, but all mingling as one mighty party. We watched until they were out of sight and sound, with the Colonel speculating as to whose winter wheat they were headed.

The wind had hardly abated at all as we sat at the gate in the Land Rover. We waited; watching until we had seen two good teams of duck, twenty or thirty in each, sweep in on set wings to the sanctuary of the broad. Then, and only then, did our host drive us back to his house. In the yard there, with steaming mugs of tea in hand, we laid out the bag. Twenty-seven duck and, except for two gadwall drakes and a pair of teal all shot by Alec, every bird was a mallard. When we were invited to select some to take home, it was the gadwall and a couple of mallard that we chose. The fact that gadwall featured in the bag explained the white speculum I thought I had seen among that team of fleeing duck. The time had come to take our leave and after thanking our genial host profusely once more, we pointed the old Ford Popular in the direction of Alec's village, and we travelled with that warm feeling of well-being and contentment that follows a morning of really good sport.

14

October 29

The next day, at least when it began, found us on a non-sporting mission. A local apple grower had been pulling out old and dead trees with a crawler tractor and had offered Alec some for firewood. We had borrowed a tractor and small trailer from George and now rattled merrily along the narrow lanes to the orchard on a fine morning. We found the dead wood hauled into a heap near the cleared ground and with a double-handed crosscut saw, cut enough into logs of a manageable length.

Alec sought out Mr Long, the owner of the orchard, to thank him for the wood. As we stood talking I noticed a small plantation of oak and beech at the edge of the property. There were several pigeons flying around it and thirty odd came over us heading for the trees. These caught Alec's eye and I saw him watch as they joined those already in residence.

"A lot of woodpigeon seem to have a liking for that little old wood." Alec said, scratching his chin thoughtfully.

"Acorns," said Mr Long, "Acorns, that's what they're after. You want to bring your gun and get yourself a pigeon pie 'bor."

"That's very kind of you," beamed Alec. "If my friend here could come too, we could perhaps try later today?"

"Oh. Do you shoot?" Said Mr Long, turning to me. "Well of course you can come - you're more than welcome."

"Well that was a bit of luck," said Alec as we drove home with our load of wood. "We can go about half-past three and stay 'til dusk and you will still have plenty of time to drive home afterwards." Back at the cottage we off-loaded the wood and carried out a sawing horse into the yard. For the next two and a half hours we sawed the lengths of apple tree into logs about eighteen inches long, and those of the largest diameter we split with sledgehammer and wedges. By the time we had finished, Alec's woodshed had a neat stack of logs ready for the fire. The few lengths we had not had time to cut up we stood in a corner of the shed to dry out ready for another sawing session. The newly cut apple wood gave off a wonderful smell, the scent of autumn, making me look forward to sharing the warmth thrown off by those logs at some later date.

Lunch that day vanished like frost before the sun, for we had worked up a healthy appetite. We even had the opportunity to relax in the armchairs before it was time to return to Mr Long's little wood. The drive there was a good deal more comfortable than before, if only because this time we were riding in Alec's Ford Popular as opposed to on George's Ford Major. We saw Mr Long emerging from one of his storage buildings. He waved and said he hoped that the pigeons were still coming to the acorns and that they would give us some good sport. On our approach, the ground beneath the trees erupted with a whirling grey and white mass of woodpigeons as they scattered in surprise. They were obviously not used to being disturbed from their cosy haven.

The first thing we did was to take a walk around the perimeter of the wood. Come to think of it 'wood' was a slightly generous description; after all it barely constituted two acres. It did not take very long to circumnavigate the plantation, but it straight away showed us where the favoured roosting trees were. The whitewash-spattered patches on the leaf floor beneath certain trees was evidence enough. Taking note of the wind direction, we selected the spots where we would stand for the last hour before dark. For the moment we moved to the edge of the wood where the pigeons had been feeding on acorns and settled down to wait. I found some good cover in a thick growth of brambles. Some long runners threatened to remove my cap each time I moved, all was well after I had used my pocketknife to trim them back Alec vanished from sight so I assumed he had found his own position.

There had been a bountiful crop of blackberries but they were now well past prime condition although there is no doubt that the birds still found them a valuable addition to their diet. A nearby hawthorn bush was a mass of colourful bright red haws. And the acorns! It is funny how some years are acorn years and others not. Without a doubt this truly was an acorn year. The floor of the wood, where we now stood hidden, was a carpet of them that crunched and moved underfoot. I cleared the area around my feet by sweeping them to one side with my boot, ensuring myself a firm footing from which to shoot.

Now where on earth did they come from..? From nowhere, in particular, seven pigeons wheeled in, ready to alight a little way down the wood. Almost as soon as I spotted them there was a puff of white feathers and one of the birds dropped. Twin reports resounded through the trees as a second bird fell from the departing pack. So, I now knew where Alec was hiding and they had not caught him napping, far from it. No more than two minutes had passed before the scene was repeated and then again! True, they were easy shots taken as the birds were about to alight, but nevertheless six woodpigeons in as many minutes is not bad by anyone's standards. I was so mesmerised by my friend's performance that when my own opportunity came I was unprepared and therefore missed. Be assured that I was concentrating after that. The pace of those first hectic few moments did not last of course, for the pigeon soon realised that something was different about the wood. All the same birds continued to attempt to resume their feed, albeit with longer intervals between our shots.

It was during such lulls, we collected the fallen. Once, I killed a high one right above the trees at the edge of the wood and almost immediately brought another crashing through the branches of a nearby beech. This bird appeared to have lodged in a fork of the tree but even as I watched, it's weight caused it to slip through and fall within a couple of yards from my position. I stooped to gather it and when I looked up again the downy feathers of a bird just shot by Alec were blowing between the tree trunks like a miniature snowstorm. All the while the trees swayed and rocked as the wind kept up a steady, relentless soft roar through the uppermost branches.

There followed quite a long period when nothing budged. My eye was then drawn to a movement, which proved to be Alec wandering around with a potato sack, picking up the slain. Following suit, I began to search for, and gather my own birds. By the time we had finished, Alec's sack

88

contained nineteen plump woodpigeon. We left them at the side of the wood and made our way to those stands selected earlier. As I hid in the undergrowth, I felt sure that I could cover most angles. There was moreover, a good gap in the trees providing a window of sky, to which I would pay particular attention. That was all well and good had the birds come in to roost, but they didn't. Perhaps all the earlier shooting had made their quarters too hot for comfort or they had decided to roost elsewhere anyway. The fact remained that not one pigeon bothered to show up. As the roosting hour came and went, we reflected on a good afternoon about which there could be no complaint. We had enjoyed good sport with the bonus of it being so close to Alec's home. We called in at the bungalow to thank Mr Long and to present him with half-a-dozen birds so that he too could enjoy a pie. His wife joined him at the door when she heard us talking and took charge of the pigeons.

"I always put a little bit of steak and some chopped onions in with the breast meat - lovely! You know what you're having on Tuesday now, Herbert," she smiled.

Mr Long grinned and turned to us.

"You want to come round again sometime, even when there are no acorns about. There's always some old woodies using that there wood and I'm rather partial to a pigeon pie topped with Joyce's short crust pastry," he said.

With visions of that feast in our minds, we left before he made us feel any hungrier.

15

November 4

The winds resulting from the autumn equinox had eased somewhat during the next week, much to the relief of householders whose slates and tiles had been sent spinning from roofs all over the county. I would suspect that the hard-pressed insurance companies were pretty pleased too. In the meantime my attention was taken up by the waxing moon, which, when full, should coincide with Alec's next visit to my neck of the woods in Cambridgeshire. Each night I watched, noting how much cloud was blowing up and what sort of backdrop it created. Of course, this can be a frustrating exercise as, however much one watches the sky, there is no guarantee that the chosen night will be blessed with the desired conditions. Moreover, a perfect sky usually turns up when for some reason or another you are unable be out under it. Thus, the opportunity to make the best of this slight advantage is lost.

I had been out on the washlands during the daytime, seeking spots where the wigeon had been feeding, but had met with no great success. True, I had found wigeon droppings around the edges of a couple of splashes of floodwater, but nothing to send one feverishly hurrying off to the ironmonger's or the gunsmith's shop for a large supply of ammunition. My friend arrived after lunch on the Saturday, commitments at work having prevented an earlier appearance. It mattered not for we were in no great hurry; in fact we relaxed during the afternoon watching a football match on the television. At half time however, we had to leave the two sides to sort out the result without our assistance. It was our intention to try an evening flight on the washes and then wait on, to see what our lunar satellite had to offer the patient sportsman.

We returned to the same area of the washes as our foray at dusk a fortnight ago, but this time we walked further along the grass drove, now muddy as a result of recent rains. At a gateway with posts that leaned at a crazy angle, we entered a block of three or four marshes that were linked by cattle bridges over rush-fringed dykes. The whole block, which extended to about thirty acres, was a low-lying mixture of tussocks and short, cattle-cropped grasses. Between the tussocks, and spilling out over the lush grass, were pools and larger flashes of floodwater. These had materialised due to a combination of the rising 'Sock' or water level beneath the turf, and the aforementioned rains.

As we entered the field gate, a dozen snipe departed noisily, followed by our muttered comments as to how skittish they were.

Alec and I split up, to splash around while searching for promising signs. At the pools I investigated an abundance of white splashes indicated visits by lapwings. I was not too encouraged by that as for some reason if plover use your chosen water, duck rarely do. Of course, that may merely be unwarranted superstition on my part, but I can only go by my long experience. In fact, as if to prove me wrong, while paddling along the lee side of a pool I immediately found a single soft brown and beige feather from the flanks of a mallard duck. The feather floated and spun high on the surface of the water. That had not been there so very long - last night at the earliest. Any longer and it would have become heavy with moisture. A shout from Alec interrupted my train of thought. He had found some wigeon droppings and was inviting me to take a look. These were certainly fresh, but I pointed out negatively that they were the result of a visit by only a very small number of birds. Jet sniffed around them - at least he showed some enthusiasm.

The plan was to move before dusk to wait by a drain that ran across the washes a little further along. We would wait there for the rising of the moon before making any further move. A leisurely stroll took us along the drove with Jet hunting in and out of the yellow rushes of the dykes. The peaty waters reminded one of Guinness, but with a rather less appetising smell. As the dog trotted by it was possible to feel a slight tremble in the soil and I told Alec that when a herd of cattle passes, the earth really does move. As we entered the marsh and set off across the sodden earth towards the drain, the sun had already begun its descent to the horizon.

The drain was twenty feet across and fringed with rushes for a further six feet on either side. Four months ago they had shone a vivid emerald green, but were now the beige of old and dusty straw. The weed growth of summer had died and sunk leaving the water looking brown and peaty in daylight. Now, one side was black in shadow whilst the other was bright with reflected light from the afterglow of the dying sun.

"If you want to get in somewhere here," I said to Alec, waving my hand in the general direction of a patch of dead and brittle thistles and nettles. "I'll move up about eighty yards or so."

Alec raised a hand in acknowledgement and turned into the cover. Instantly, with a clattering of wings that made us both jump, a cock pheasant headed skywards like a high velocity bullet. At the peak of his climb he collapsed and fell to my friend's shot.

"Phew! Damn good job I haven't got a weak heart," laughed Alec, clutching his chest in a theatrical manner. "That old blighter could have finished me off, sitting there as tight as that." Jet brought the bird to hand. The old cock had indeed sat very tight, no doubt hoping that we would pass him by so that he could stay in his intended jugging hollow for the night. He had chosen a good spot too - good cover, cosy bed of grasses. Had it been daylight we might have found his droppings, and perhaps evidence of more than one night's stay in these particular lodgings. It was his bad luck that we had chanced to turn up at that moment and unluckier still that he did not take Alec completely by surprise. It was surely fate that decreed he should now recline at the bottom of Alec's game-bag, his long, barred tail peeping from the top.

The excitement of the bonus pheasant was forgotten for the moment as we took up our positions at the side of the drain to keep watch on the western sky. During our vigil we were at least spared the torment of the hordes of gnats and mosquitoes that were such a nuisance in September. With the dusk came a wind from the southwest. It was not much more than a breeze, but unusual in that winds usually die at the approach of nightfall. Lapwing came, wailing low and unseen over the marshes, the 'frow, frow' of their wing-beats caught the ear as they passed in darkness, but not far away. The scraping calls of snipe approached, until with a tearing sound the little birds plummeted to earth in peregrine-like stoops. Some, we could see momentarily against the light and we even managed to bag three. There is usually a reasonable gap between the time snipe drop in and when duck arrive; nevertheless after we had contrived to miss a dozen we stopped, in case our shots put off any early duck. We need not have worried too much. The early evening's flypast consisted of one team of mallard that went wide of Alec and a singleton that came nicely towards me. At the last moment the duck veered off presenting a long shot, if it was a shot at all. By the time I had hesitated it had cleared off altogether.

We returned to the field gate and leant thereon as we shared a hot drink from a thermos flask. The moon had risen huge and yellow in the east, and now gradually receded in size as it climbed ever higher. There were a few clouds, but the background they provided could hardly be described as favourable. However, there was a far more extensive bank of cloud moving up, blown steadily by the wind. Making our way back along the drove, we soon retraced our steps to the wet and rough block of marshes. There was not a lot of cover to be found, but one could kneel among the tussocks and rely on keeping absolutely still. The art of keeping still is essential. You can hide behind a single thistle if you keep still - movement is an instant giveaway. So, we selected our flooded patches and settled down to wait. I found a good clump of tussocks not far from the water's edge. As I knelt the cover almost came up to my shoulders, which was heartening. My range of vision was perhaps forty yards in which everything was captured in varying shades of grey. The only exception was the brilliant silver reflection of the moon's bright beam on the shallow water. The water had spread hither and thither over the short grass and between the tussocks in an irregular pattern. Even in this light, seeds could be seen floating in patches along the edges. It certainly looked as though it ought to be attractive to all manner of wildfowl.

Readjusting my position, I thought I heard the whistle of a wigeon, but then wondered whether my movement had caused my boots to squeak. Clothing and footwear can play all sorts of tricks on the hearing. Minute creaks and rubs might sound uncannily like a goose or some other fowl, heard faintly in the distance. Remembering the advice of an old mentor of mine I turned one ear into the wind and listened intently with the other, mouth half open in concentration. Then it came again - definitely wigeon, definitely on the move and more than one at that. Exciting moments as a goodly company came and passed on the far side of the drove until the sound of their calling faded away. A whicker of wings from behind, close ... where the devil? The strange call of a gadwall identified this visitor and seconds later the swish as it, or they, pitched onto the water far behind me.

The bank of cloud had arrived now and moreover, it was of the fleecy consistency that wildfowlers pray for and seldom get. The moon shone wanly behind the thin veil, illuminating the clouds beautifully. I gazed at the sky, taking in the magic of being out on such a lovely night and absentmindedly watched as a black shadow slid downwards across the pale clouds. Suddenly the shadow burst into a dozen pieces and vanished, except for one fragment that plummeted down. Then came the sound of the report, even as the sudden white splash of water showed where the duck had hit the surface. My goodness, they had slipped in quietly. I could see Alec clearly as he stooped to collect his prize. A few minutes later more wigeon arrived just as silently. They were almost down before my eyes caught the movement, but as I fired and dropped the first bird the others flew momentarily into a light patch of sky allowing me to complete the right and left without too much difficulty. Jet darted off for the furthest of the fallen while I walked over to the nearer one. At first I couldn't see it anywhere, but then I spotted a gleam of white near a tussock. It turned out to be the belly of a fine cock wigeon. Jet came snuffling up with the other duck and we hurried back to our hiding place. For half an hour there were wigeon on the move. Sometimes they advertised their presence by whistling and growling, other times not. Black dots hurtled across the sky, black dots on swivelling wings swung over the water right in front of either one or the other of us. Wings that tore through the air, so close, yet passing unseen on the dark side of our marsh. Then came a lull, after which we heard wigeon on the far side of the drove. Soon, nothing moved. Alec drew himself to his feet stiffly and splashed over to me.

"Well," he said. "They certainly made their minds up to dine here tonight. I'm glad we didn't reject these fields after all - that was a damned good flight."

Sentiments shared, we strolled homewards along the drove under the bright moon. Eleven fat wigeon along with our snipe and the bonus pheasant added a comfortable weight to our side bags. It felt good to have luck on our side.

16

November 5

The next morning, as I was spreading a thick layer of marmalade onto a slice of toast, I suggested that we return to the scene of last night's adventure. My wife looked up saying.

"I didn't think you could shoot duck on a Sunday here."

"You can't, but I thought we could all go for some fresh air and have a look at those flashes in daylight."

"Sounds like a good idea to me." said Alec. With that we stacked the breakfast things into the sink for attention later, and set off. As we motored along at a leisurely forty-five miles per hour, I amused Alec by telling him of an incident when my wife's nephew and his girlfriend came over from Germany to stay with us. It was the act of placing the breakfast dishes into the sink that had reminded me.

Micky was the son of my wife's brother who had been posted to Germany as a serviceman. He had met and married a local girl and had settled down over there. Naturally, Mickey was fluent in the languages of both parents. He and his girlfriend Klaudia would have been about thirty years old, at the time of the visit. My wife was at work, so I kept the couple entertained by taking them to local places of interest. On the first morning Klaudia insisted on washing up after breakfast, but placing them under lid of the sink I stopped her.

"It's all right. We'll leave them under here and perhaps the elves will wash them while we are away," I said. I thought no more about it, but obviously the girl had taken in what I had said because the next morning, as I turned on the tap to run hot water into the sink, Klaudia skipped into the kitchen. With arms outstretched as though flying, she sang, "I vill be an elf, I vill be an elf". Mickey gazed at her and without batting an eyelid, snorted.

"Ach! No vonder the Germans lost the var!" I collapsed with laughter - who said the Germans have no sense of humour?

At the washes we strolled along the riverbank until we were opposite 'our' block of marsh. A distant white smudge turned out to be a party of gulls and with the aid of binoculars we could see a dozen teal swimming to one side of them. Closer inspection revealed several more moving between the tussocks and rushes and further over still, the heads and necks of some mallard suddenly appeared. It was not possible to see how many exactly, for as some were lost to view, others reared up. Large groups of starlings flitted noisily from place to place among the shallow pools and flashes. We could only think that they were feeding on the floating seeds. As is often the case at the time of full moon, the morning was clear and bright, with a clean, crisp freshness to the air. There wasn't a frost, but the temperature could not have been far above freezing point when we deserted our beds a few hours earlier. I have often surprised our children, by accurately predicting a month or more in advance that certain dates will be fine and sunny. They thought I was some sort of gifted meteorologist until I explained that the dates were on or around the full moon. It is then that the skies are more likely to be clear at night, which greatly increases the chances of it being a fine day on the morrow. There is a certain amount of luck involved of course and it does not always work out, but on the whole it is a pretty reliable form of guestimate.

The three of us walked for another mile or so before retracing our steps, and all the time spotting parties of duck on the multitude of pools and shallow splashes. When viewed from our slightly higher vantage point on the riverbank, they shone like scattered fragments of a shattered mirror. A hundred wigeon flew along the washes in a long arc formation. As they passed, one or two pintail could be seen amongst their number. On the homeward journey we stopped off at a public house for bread, strong cheese and pickled onions, washed down with a pint of the landlord's best bitter.

Back home, we spent the rest of the afternoon in quiet relaxation, reading the papers with a hand or two of cards. I was shuffling the pack ready to deal when Alec spoke.

"Do you fancy a run down the marsh later?"

I had been thinking along the same lines, but Alec had suggested it first and I hastily agreed with him. "Yes, we'll aim to get away in an hour and see if the cloud is kind to us." In a little under the hour we were cruising towards the coast, full of optimism and speculation. If the cloud comes up... If the wind would increase just a touch, wouldn't it be lucky if...

High tide had been at six o'clock so there had been an hour's ebb before we rolled up at the base of the sea wall. The moon, which hung like a huge Chinese lantern not far above the horizon, welcomed us, but she would soon shrink and rise higher into the night sky. There was not much by way of cloud, but there was a bit of wind and we knew from experience how quickly the scene could change. For ease of walking we clumped along the track on the landward side of the sea bank and made good progress until, after half a mile we climbed the bank to get our bearings. It was truly magical. The whole estuary, bathed in a soft silvery light stretched away before us, and the slightly elevated position afforded us from the top of the sea wall gave us a grandstand view. Even though the tide had receded to the far fringe of the saltings, there was enough water remaining in some of the wider creeks to reflect the moonlight, which exposed their meanderings through the crabgrass and sea aster stalks. We stood for some time absorbing this enchanting scene. After all, there was no hurry and it was well worth more than a casual glance. Eventually we made the short walk that would bring us to the point where we planned to gain access to the marsh.

Some cloud had drifted up and was at the moment, nicely illuminated by the moon, so we scrambled down the bank and made our way out onto the marsh.

"There should be a good flash about two hundred yards further on," I said to Alec, as we plodded steadfastly onwards, brushing through the knee-high crab grass. It's little oval leaves were sage green in daylight, but turned soft grey in the lunar light.

"I can see it," said Alec. "It's over there, a bit to the right." And so it was. The crab grass gave way to something akin to a rough meadow grass. Certainly, the cattle that had access to the marsh until October seemed to find it palatable, and the fact that they had grazed it short was all too the good. The short grass was at a slightly lower level than the crab grass and the receding tide had left the pan brimming with water. How could a wigeon resist it? Taking an end each we knelt, both on one knee and watched and waited. The seconds and minutes ticked by as our knees gradually settled in the liquid mud.

Everything in the garden was looking good, until that sparse cloud cover disappeared as quickly as it arrived, leaving us with the moon, surrounded by bright twinkling stars in an inky firmament. It would be hard to catch sight of duck now even if we were graced with their presence.

"You might get a glimpse as they hover before landing." Alec murmured, as though reading my negative thoughts.

"You might," I agreed, half-heartedly.

It is possible to shoot birds in that narrow strip of reflected light above the water, but you have to be looking in exactly the right place at the right nano-second, and you have to be quick.

We hung on for another hour hoping against hope that more cloud would appear, but our luck was out. However, even we had cloud, it would not have changed the fact that there were no wigeon on the move. I had heard one solitary whistle soon after we had ventured out onto the marsh, but since then nothing. Only once, did I grip the gun in readiness that night and then relaxed, as the distinctive whistle of the pinions identified my intended victim as a shelduck. I caught sight of it briefly, as it passed overhead, going about its business. The lovely bubbling calls of curlew could be heard along the tide-line as more, and still more feeding grounds revealed themselves to those long probing bills, but there were no duck. The mallard had gone in, to the fields long ago of course, and were even now, probably guzzling rotting potatoes between the rows of some unsuspecting farmer's winter wheat. But where were the wigeon? The answer to that question remained a mystery.

At last I stood up and stretched to push circulation back through cramped legs. I heard my companion get up, though the light was such that I could not see him. His footsteps came splashing through the shallows until he appeared wraith-like from a backdrop of uniform greyness. Back on the sea wall we sat down to burn a pipe of tobacco, and all the time listening for the call of wigeon and watching for even a mere wisp of a cloud. A hint of either, and Alec and I would have gone back out. We eventually admitted defeat and sauntered to where the car was parked. No trip is ever wasted though I reflected, staring out over the sparkling vista of this remote foreshore.

17

November 11

Alec and Tom were staying at my house again so that we could make an early start, ensuring our arrival at the farm of a friend of mine well before light. We hoped for a morning flight of duck along a tidal river that bordered one side of the farm. Frankly, we were taking potluck, because there was no regular flight along this river. Some days you find duck there, some day's you don't, but what are wildfowlers if not optimists?

After an uneventful journey, traversing miles of narrow, straight and uneven roads, with reed-filled dykes on either side, we found ourselves passing through Chris's yard. There were lights on in the house and a storm lantern glowed in one of the farm buildings, but we didn't stop. Chris knew we were coming and I didn't want to interrupt the start of his working day. Passing through the yard and onto a rough track, we drove on for another half mile until the track petered out at a riverbank of sea wall proportions. Parallel to the bank, and some hundred and fifty yards out on the landward side, ran a steep-sided drain. Between the two waterways was the rough pasture grazed by Chris's cattle or sheep.

I led the way under the lee of the bank heading for a fence that I knew would provide cover of sorts. Even in darkness, when you know a place well, certain landmarks can be used as reminders of your exact position. For example when passing the pinprick of lights showing in the windows of a far distant house, or a cattle pen, you rest easy, familiar with these year on year fixtures. One could use straw stacks, but of course they are not so permanent. I kept my eyes on my favoured landmarks as we moved steadily on.

Beyond the all-enfolding blanket of the pre-dawn darkness there was no visible sign of livestock on the bank, but the pungent smell of sheep was so strong on the air that it was evident that a flock was not too far away. Two more paces forward and a muffled rumbling told its story of a substantial number of sheep scurrying off, collecting more and more of the flock as they hurried past their dozing comrades. After a hundred yards or so, it dawned on them that whatever it was that had come upon them so silently, it was not chasing them. Before very long they had quietened down until all that could be heard was the occasional cough and wheeze, sounding not unlike an early morning smoker shortly after lighting up his first woodbine of the day.

Before long the chosen fence loomed up and we slackened our pace, for we were well in time. Parts of the fence, including the gate posts, were stout railway sleepers and near the brink of the river there were wooden rails to prevent attempts by livestock to get round the end. The fence provided excellent cover, but only from birds approaching from one way. To give cover on the unprotected side it was easy enough to collect rubbish from the jetsam line of the last spring tide. On this occasion we found a wooden pallet, which was almost enough to complete the hide. I invited Alec and Tom to man the rough hide, whilst I moved a hundred yards downstream. The tide was ebbing so any birds falling into the river would be bound to float down to me in due course, and I had the dog. I found a little curve in the grass and mud at the river's edge where I could perch near to the mud shelf, which sloped gently to the river, four feet in front of me. A thick growth of rushes gave further cover. I was still warm with the exertion of the hurried walk and pallet hauling, so it was comfortable in my little niché as I watched the morning break.

The day began still and quiet, hardly a proper fowling morning. At least, it was quiet until there came a noise that can only be described as a distant clanging rumble. It was a sound that might puzzle someone who had never heard a load of sugar beet being tipped into the steel hull of an empty trailer, but at this time of year it is an everyday sight and sound in beet country.

By now I could easily see the far side of the river and anticipating the chance of a shot, I took the opportunity to check again that my gun barrels were clear of obstruction. A mere breath of sound from behind caused me to turn. There, just feet away, a short-eared owl glided around, twisting it's moon-like face to get a better look at me. Curiosity satisfied, the bird flapped off, probably to check out Alec. Then I glimpsed a movement on the far bank. Whatever it was had become concealed in the rough grasses. As I watched the spot, a hare suddenly emerged, loping along in a relaxed, unconcerned style. I squeaked the palm of my hand and she stopped and sat, ears erect for a moment before moving off with no particular sense of urgency. She had been in range for a long shot, indeed I had shot just such a hare in the past, but I did not want one this morning. Anyway a hare that has been retrieved over a river is wet, bedraggled and all in all a pitiful sight, so I was happy to watch as puss went about her business unhindered.

On whistling pinions came a dozen mallard scything across the sky, high overhead. I watched them follow the course of the river until they were out of sight, but as I stared into the distance a gang of teal belted by within range. It was their flaring and panicked climb that attracted my attention, but by then it was too late even to raise the gun. Twenty more teal pitched onto the river a quarter of a mile downstream and began feeding along the muddy edge. Ten minutes later another little party approached and I was surprised when they did not join the others. Instead they came on - I was going to get a shot. They were in view all the time, flying rapidly along the river, only thirty feet above the surface of the silky tide. Swinging up the old magnum I blotted one out and squeezed the trigger. I was amazed when the bird did not fall and fired the second barrel in a hurry, missing again. I just could not believe it. Then I heard Alec shooting and looked his way, in time to see a little shape splash down into the river. I kept my eye on the dead teal as it floated towards me on the tide, waiting for the moment to send Jet leaping into the water to retrieve. Nothing else flew so after another half an hour I walked back towards the fence to be greeted by Alec wearing a broad grin.

"How *did* you miss them?" He jibed, enjoying the fact that he had wiped my eye as the teal accelerated away from me.

"Those cartridges were loaded with salt," I replied, making a mental note to return the favour as soon as the opportunity arose! Tom did not pass comment, but I noticed a quiet smile cross his face as he listened to our banter.

As we drove back to my house I told them a story of a friend who had been duck shooting with my brother. They had been youths at the time and my friend Jim favoured a five-shot automatic. Some teal had come high over them and Jim had fired causing them to rocket straight up, whereupon he emptied his magazine at them. When the first duck hit the ground my brother had said - "Phew! That was a damned good shot." To which Jim replied, "What about these others then?" As five more teal dropped all around them. Thump! Ththumpety! Thump! More by luck than judgment one shot had killed one, another shot two and another - three. "If I hadn't seen that with my own eyes I would never have believed it," my brother exclaimed.

"Well, remember it because I bet I'll never, ever do it again," said a breathless Jim.

We hadn't forgotten it was Armistice Day and we quietly observed the two-minute silence at eleven o'clock. After a light lunch, we were ready to be on the move once more. I suggested we have a run out to the washes to see if any more snipe had arrived. We filled our pockets with number seven and eight shot cartridges and set off. We were soon bumping and splashing along the muddy track, until we came to a small bridge that was just large enough to take farm trailers and implements. Here we drew off the track and parked on a grassy verge. While we were donning our thigh boots Jet was busily investigating every gatepost, thistle, and clump of rushes - in fact everything he could possibly cram in before he was called to heel. I have mixed feelings about taking a dog snipe shooting, especially on a calm day such as this, because of the additional splashing they create when you are endeavouring to make a quiet approach. On the other hand, unless it falls belly up, a dead snipe is very difficult to find by sight among the beige and rust coloured grasses and rushes. Then the faithful hound is invaluable.

There was no decision to make this afternoon, Jet was here and Jet was coming. Off we went, further along the muddy track, taking in our surroundings as we walked. We passed through a five-barred gate after which the drove was grass-covered. Although the ground still squelched underfoot, the haymakers' vehicles had not cut it up during the summer so the going was slightly easier. After a hundred yards or so the drove divided, straight on, or a ninety-degree turn to the left. We took the left turn for it would bring us out into the middle of a broad expanse of cattle marshes. On either side of the rutted track were partly rush-filled dykes although the water did show up from time to time. We walked with care for it was not that unusual to surprise duck that had chosen to lie up for the day. Suddenly, with a harsh "Fraaank!" a heron, looking enormous at such close quarters, launched itself from almost under our feet. It is not often one gets so close to the old harnser, he usually spots potential trouble a mile off. This one had been right down in the dyke and for those few moments had dropped his guard. He flapped off, croaking in a most disgruntled manner.

By way of a further gate, we entered a chain of washes linked by culverted earth dams. Spreading out, we tramped the whole half-mile length without flushing a single bird within range. The only snipe we saw, departed when we were at least three gunshots off. Back out onto the drove again we strode on until I found the ligger I was looking for. This one was a stout railway sleeper laid across the dyke, giving us access to another block of marshes. It took a bit of finding among the rushes, but it saved us a half-mile walk to get round to the same spot. We negotiated it without being knocked off by the dog, which would insist on trying to push by when one was teetering precariously halfway across. These marshes were wetter and dotted with thick tussocks, some standing shoulder high. There were more snipe here, but again they were flushing wild. As I meandered between the tussocks, five teal erupted from a small splash nearby. As they reached the peak of their climb, I fired, sending one tumbling down. At the shot, a hare started ahead of us and sprinted away causing spray to fly from the wet places in her path. We had the makings of a bag now and by the end of the block we had added two snipe to the tally.

Our next port of call was a familiar chain of marshes, scene of our moonlight wigeon flight a week ago. We stood at the field gate for a rest and enjoyed a leisurely smoke. After tapping out our pipes on the gatepost we continued by taking a dyke each, walking steadily out into the swampier parts. The short grasses and cattle-cropped rushes here were still a vivid emerald green on account of the water around their roots. This place must be heaving with worms, dead and alive; it must surely be snipe heaven! On...on... every step sounding dreadfully loud with the dog making his contribution to the perceived din. Yet we could not have been so noisy for snipe did sit. A rustle to my left alerted me to a snipe jumping not above ten yards away, white feathers flashing. Even as I whipped the gun up to my shoulder, a second bird rose from the same spot. As a rule, the snipe blend well into the background, aided by poor light, but not so today - luck was on my side for once. Caught in the low sunlight, the jinking longbills showed up clearly and both spun down to my double shot. Right and left! Now that did not often happen for me on the snipe marsh. Alec waved his congratulations, but wisely remained focused while I picked up my birds. I say picked them, but that was easier said than done. Even though I had marked them well and knew from bitter experience not to take my eyes off the spot, it was several minutes before they were both in the bag. The first wasn't so bad. I could see its white under-wing long before I reached it, but the second bird proved to be more difficult. In fact I never saw the bird at all until Jet suddenly dipped his head down among the rushes and came out with it. Without him, I felt sure that snipe would have been lost.

I moved on, full of confidence with the glow of my right and left to the foremost of my thoughts. At each step half expecting that sudden "scrape" of a rising snipe. The next one flitted up right in front, but further out. My shot was clearly visible as a cloud of fine spray, whipped up a good foot behind the snipe, which twisted away to the right and presented Alec with an opportunity for a fine crossing shot. I saw the bird drop a split-second before the sound of the shot reached me. Alec grinned across at me; he had wiped my eye again - twice in one day. This had got to stop! We splashed on, trying to keep abreast with one another. A further forty yards through and eight snipe got up together. Six shots rang out, but not one bird fell. We walked and splashed and stumbled, stumbled, splashed and walked on. We hunted all the likely places, finding snipe in a few spots here and there, whereas marshes that looked equally attractive to us, held no birds at all. Some birds found their way into the bag, whilst many more were missed. Even Tom, who had never shot snipe before, collected a couple, capping off a glorious afternoon, one that we all remembered for a long time afterwards.

18

November 12

A complete change in the weather came as a surprise when we rose in the morning. On opening the back door in preparation for a drive to the coast, we were greeted by a swirling fog. It wasn't too bad however, and after only a very brief moment of hesitation we elected to go ahead as planned. Although the fog was patchy it was enough to make the drive a bit of a strain as we peered wide-eyed through the windscreen, as the wipers flip-flopped in a continuous attempt to flick away the clinging moisture. Three pairs of eyes stared into the glare of the headlights reflected back off the bank of fog, attempting to glimpse the roadside verges and to ensure that we spotted in time any unforeseen obstacles on unlit and unlined country roads. They were fen roads, which meant that for the most part there were no hedges or trees to act as markers. Instead there were deep ditches. If a vehicle runs off the road into one it is not necessarily life threatening, but it is definitely the end of any particular excursion. Our journey seemed to take three times as long as it did normally, although in reality it took only a little longer. All the same, I think we were all pleased when we turned onto the track that led to the sea wall.

After I had switched off the ignition we sat for a little while in the car, so that our eyes could adjust to the changed circumstances, and then when we were all ready we set off along the familiar drove-way at the base of the sea wall. It was relatively mild for the time of year and after walking for half an hour, in several layers of clothing, we were all pretty warm. Once we set foot on the marsh we were forced to reduce the pace and so cooled to a more comfortable temperature. Here on the shore, the fog was very much thicker. As it was still dark, our progress out over the saltings was slow. For ease of walking we clambered down to the hard bottom of a large creek and in single file, with young Tom in the middle, we followed its winding course until at last it reached, what is known locally, as the stalk edges. That is to say, the point where the green marsh ends and the mud flats stretch away for miles into The Wash. Just before we reached the mud, Alec hauled himself up out of the creek and stood up. There was a second's pause and then we were startled by an almighty sound, not unlike a roll of thunder, followed by the clamour of a sizeable number of pinkfooted geese. We didn't see a thing, but stood gaping in amazement as the voices of the geese drifted faintly back as they headed out to sea.

"My godfathers!" Alec gasped. "The tide must have set them down here last night and when the fog rolled up they stayed put. I've heard of people walking into them and getting a shot in those circumstances. No chance of that this morning though."

"Right Tom," Said I. "We'll spread out along the edge of the marsh and hope that the fog clears a bit at dawn so that the geese feel like coming in. You go along there with Alec and stay where he puts you. The tide's not due until about eleven and even then it will hardly get into the marsh. All the same, it would not be very pleasant to feel that you were lost out here. So don't move and we'll know where to find you. We won't be far away in any case. There's no guarantee those geese will come in this way, so if you get a chance at a duck, take it."

Alec led the way with Tom close on his heels and within seconds they had vanished into the fog, like an actor stepping behind a curtain.

Jet looked up as if to ask whether we were going too, but when I slithered back down into the creek he accepted the fact that for the time being, we were going nowhere. There was no need to kneel even when it became lighter, because anything that came into my field of view would be well in range. For two hours we hung on hoping for a break in that grey blanket. During all that time we saw neither hide nor hair of any living thing. The only sound belonged to the salt water, trickling and gurgling through myriad minor gutters and creeklets. It was a sound that served only to emphasise the eerie isolation of our surroundings.

After a while, muffled voices alerted me to the fact that the others were making their way back along the shoreline. Suddenly the pair materialised out of the damp, clinging greyness, and we stood speculating as to whether or not the fog would ever clear. We decided that it would not, and it was time to head for the car. Prior to our trek back along the big creek, we set about unloading our guns. "There's a big old gull coming. That's the first bird I've seen all morning," said Tom, sounding surprised.

Alec looked up. "That's not a gull - it's a flipping goose. Get ready Tom, our guns are empty." It was a goose for sure, and not six feet, above the mud, coming straight for us and the three of us caught out in the open. Even if there had been time for Alec and I to fumble for cartridges, the movement would not have been missed, so we froze. Tom completely misjudged the speed of the bird and it was far too close when he threw up his gun. I don't think the goose had spotted us until that moment. The bird flared and climbed over Tom's head making him duck down. We looked on helplessly as the lad stumbled round to fire at the rapidly disappearing pinkfoot. The great bird did not even flinch as it flew steadily on until it was lost to sight. Poor Tom's face was a picture of misery and we were sensitive enough not to rub it in with our usual banter. A miss at an easy pheasant is one thing, but to miss the gift of a chance to bag one's first pinkfoot, is quite another matter. Alec broke the awful silence.

"Funny him coming in like that, he must have got separated from his skein and got lost."

"Speaking of becoming lost, Tom," I added hastily, "you will read a lot about the need to carry a compass when you are wildfowling, in case the fog rolls in whilst you are out here. Well, it's good advice and we always carry compasses, but you must have a sound knowledge of your marsh as well. What I mean is, if you are caught out by fog and on a rising tide, it's not a bit of good knowing the right direction to the sea wall if between you and it, there's a wide creek in the way."

I continued with my marsh lesson-cum-distraction ploy. "If you're out on featureless sands your compass should get you back to the salt-marsh, but once there you need to be able to recognise the main creeks and channels. I can only speak for this marsh, where the unwritten rule is that wildfowlers do not venture out onto the mud. If a big tide is due to flood while you are out on the marsh, The best plan is to follow a large creek out, making sure that you do not cross any side gutters that you cannot jump. Then if it turns foggy, you can simply follow your creek back to the sea wall. You can still get disorientated of course, but then you have your compass to put you back on the right track."

By the time I had explained all this, the initial sting of missing the goose had faded and Tom's natural good humour had returned. However I decided that it was not the appropriate time to tell him about a local gunsmith who found himself on the inland washes when the fog clamped down. A small party of whitefronts suddenly came out of the fog, right over his head. The geese saw him at the same moment, swerved and bunched. There must have been several necks together at the same time for when he fired once, three or four geese came tumbling down.

Our drive home in daylight was better, and whilst still foggy, it became clearer away from the coast. It had been a blank morning as far as the game book was concerned, but both Alec and I agreed that it had been a valuable experience for our youthful trainee.

19

November 17

Alec and I were enjoying our shooting, and the next adventure could never come round soon enough. So it was that I found myself back in Norfolk before very long. On my arrival I found Alec hovering impatiently, in the yard behind the cottage. I knew I wasn't late, so winding down the window I enquired if everything was all right.

"Oh yes," he replied, "It's just that there have been a few duck using the river by Uncle Edgar's water meadows and we've just about got time to get down there before dusk."

Never one to miss an impromptu duck flight, I dumped my holdall in the kitchen and quickly changed into an old pair of trousers. Then hurried out to join an impatient Alec. He had already thrown my shooting jacket and gun into the back of his car, alongside Rosy. To the accompanying sounds of grating gears and a revving engine, the little Ford lurched out of the yard and shot off through the village. Tom's parents lived in a cottage just on the outskirts and as it came into view I could see a figure standing near the gate looking up

116

the road in our direction. The figure was carrying a gun. It appeared that Tom was ready.

Ten minutes later the three of us were out of the car and walking by the side of a hedge on the gentle slope down to the river. The hedge petered out on the lower meadows to be replaced by a barbed wire fence. Where the fence reached the brink of the river it was stapled to a row of three huge willow trees. These willows had obviously been pollarded at some time in the past, but judging from the growth in their tops, had not been trimmed for a good many years.

This meadow was one of a chain of four providing grazing for Edgar's cattle and sheep. A small bunch of bullocks came charging up to investigate the strangers in their domain. They stood around us puffing and blowing, whilst snuffling at Rosy. Alec suggested that I walk down to the furthest fence, while Tom made a hiding place near the one midway between us. When we had collected enough dead sticks from around the willows, Tom and I walked to the fence and quickly constructed a rough screen for the lad to hide behind. I then left him, to follow the curve of the river. A snipe jumped from the rushes fringing the brink and I thought of taking the shot, but it flew out over the river so I held my fire. It would not be fair to call Alec to bring Rosy, this close to dusk. Even so, as an enthusiastic snipe shooter I have to say that I was sorely tempted!

The river straightened out for a little way before looping sharply round to the right. After the bend it swung back, almost on its original course. Right at the start of the bend stood the fence where I was to wait. A shallow ditch, allowing some drainage of the meadows, entered the river at this point and meandered right back to the rising ground a quarter of a mile away. The fence, which was wired with sheep mesh, followed the course of the ditch. A low blackthorn bush grew twenty yards in from the waters edge and behind this I chose to hide. I was hoping that any duck flying along the river would cut the corner at the bend.

The sun was nearly below the horizon by this time and whilst some creatures were thinking of sleep, for others this was a time when they became active. Outlined on the horizon was quite a large area of hawthorn scrub, dotted here and there with stunted oaks that protruded stark and leafless above that wild patch. With a rattle of wings, a cock pheasant launched himself from the rough cover below the scrub and sailed over the river. I saw him briefly against the orange sky. Doubtless, he was making for a spinney behind me, where I had already heard some of his clan cocking up to roost. There was a clap and clatter, as a party of woodpigeon settled in one of the oaks. Despite the distance, I could see each individual bird dotted like fruit on the tree; surely they didn't intend to roost in that unsheltered spot?

I would never know the answer because the silence was shattered by a double shot from downstream. Not long afterwards, a duck came into view, flying straight along the river. I was preparing to swing the gun up when, at the last moment, I saw another pair to the left of the singleton and these were cutting the corner. They came straight and true looking, as one well-known author has described them, like hock bottles with wings. Due to the light, there was time for one shot only, but that also proved to be straight and true. The following bird of the pair shut its wings and plummeted to earth. And yes, it was the second bird I had fired at because I knew this would be the drake. I walked out to find him and after a moment the white underside of one of the wings revealed his position among the short meadow grasses. It was then that I looked again at the oak tree and was not surprised to see its branches devoid of pigeons.

The light had gone so I strolled leisurely back to the others, enjoying the peace of this tranquil evening. Tom had fired that first shot, and he held up a mallard duck in answer to my enquiry as to his luck. Alec had heard us coming and we could just discern his shadowy form making its way back to the high ground. At his heel trotted Rosy, followed in turn, by a skittish mob of bullocks. We angled across the meadow and joined them.

Later that evening, by mutual consent, we gave our brace of duck to Edgar as a small token of our appreciation. This pleasant duty performed, the three of us repaired to the village pub for a pint, where we found a corner table unoccupied by the Friday crowd of regulars. Without really thinking about it, I must have been rambling on about my native fens and the wildfowling to be had there in far off days because it prompted Tom.

"What were the fens like a hundred years ago?" he asked.

Alec gasped in mock amazement.

"What? Fancy asking him that - we'll be here all night now, see you in about three hours!"

With that he lounged back in his chair and began the ritual of packing his pipe, lighting it, tamping down the singed tobacco and lighting it again, properly.

The question had taken me rather by surprise, so I took advantage of the next few moments whilst we were trying to peer at each other across a table temporarily engulfed by a dense blue fug, to reflect and to compose in my mind a brief but hopefully concise reply.

"Well, although we still call the district, 'Fenland' there is not much left that could be described as 'fen' using the proper definition of the word. A fen is boggy land with a high water table and a good deal of standing water. True, the modern fenland is still a watery environment, but man

119

controls that water, for most of the time at least. It's drained from the land and pumped into the main rivers, from where any unwanted surplus is discharged into the sea by way of tidal rivers and of course, on a favourable ebb tide.

"Two hundred years ago it was a very different matter, the area was much wetter, especially in winter. In that wet season vast tracts of land were laid waste when inundated by floodwater from higher land in the surrounding counties. To answer your question, the mid-nineteenth century had seen improvements in drainage that resulted in most of the fen district remaining dry throughout the year. Much of the high land floodwater was held, as it is today, on the large areas of washland specially created for the job, but there remained pockets of exceptionally low-lying land where the water settled naturally. These were the Meres. The largest of these shallow lakes took on the name of the nearest town or village - Ramsey, Soham, Benwick and the greatest of them all - Whittlesey Mere. Although the town of Whittlesey is in Cambridgeshire, its Mere was situated four miles from the town, across the county boundary in Huntingdonshire. With a water area of 1600 acres in summer, which almost doubled to 3000 acres in the winter months, Whittlesey Mere was the largest lake in southern England.

The gentry fished, sailed and held regattas there during the summer, and one or two had their own boat dyke complete with thatched boathouses. The most famous of these was perhaps Lord Sandwich who lived with his family, the Montagues, at Barnwell in Northamptonshire. Barnwell was not far to travel by horse and carriage and it is easy to imagine His Lordship and the family trotting down to the fen to enjoy a day on their yacht, also named Sandwich. Indeed, on the old maps there was a peninsular jutting out into the Mere that was named Sandwich Point. You can be sure that the family would be well provisioned with hams, game pies, jars of pickles, stone jars of beer from Smith's brewery in Oundle, and bottles of port. It would have been sensible to retain a fenman to look after the yacht in their absence, and if they did I'll bet there was much competition for the job."

I looked at Tom through the fog of pipe smoke. He was all ears so, needing little encouragement, I continued.

"The nearest settlements to the Mere were villages such as Yaxley, Farcet and Holme and their populations provided the labour for the annual cycle of fishing, 'fowling and reed harvest. No part of the Mere was ever deeper than six feet, and it had even been known to dry out completely in drought summers, with disastrous consequences for the thriving fish stocks. The fenmen were always on the lookout for ways to add a few more coppers to their income. Their great knowledge of the home environment guaranteed that they were much sought after by visiting naturalists who employed them as guides in their search for rare birds or insects. Many of them were undergraduates from the Cambridge colleges. These young men arrived loaded with tin boxes and jars for specimens, and they were glad enough to pay to be shown the best places to find their intended quarry. To be sure, they would have been most unlikely to find anything at all if they ventured out on their own. In fact, they would be very lucky if they did not become hopelessly lost in the acres of tall reeds.

The local man on the spot took daily note of where, for example, a bearded tit or a harrier was nesting. At the appropriate time and for the right price, he could lead his client right to it. That was important because to the majority of the Victorian collectors, a specimen was worthless unless they had taken it with their own hand. I can remember when the museum at Peterborough had a Natural History room with cases of mounted butterflies and stuffed birds, not to mention drawers full of beetles. I imagine that most, if not all, of those specimens came from the collections of those long dead old boys who haunted the wild places clasping net and moth lamp. As a youth I visited that room many times. I cannot recall all I saw then, but I remember that there was a shoveler midway between its autumn and winter plumage. The cases that fascinated me most were two tall glass cases with white labels that read - *White-tailed Sea Eagle, shot at Whittlesea Mere 1830* and - *Great White Stork, shot at Thorney Fen 1830.* These two great birds seemed almost as tall as I was, and I was always drawn to them. I wonder where they are now?

In another part of the museum they had a boat that was completely covered with a deck, rather like a lid. The whole vessel was perforated with hundreds of holes and it was used for storing live eels. I have since seen and used eel trunks, which are similar, but never one shaped like a boat. When I left the museum I usually headed for to the cattle market, because there was a man there who sold second-hand guns. He would have an assortment of, what might be termed 'farm guns', spread out on rugs on the ground. Usually hammer-guns, there was occasionally a worm-eaten muzzle-loader among them, and all were offered for sale in exchange for a few pounds. There were also boxes filled with copper powder flasks, others with leather shot flasks and miscellaneous shooting paraphernalia. It was never less than fascinating to me.

But, going back to Whittlesey Mere. Just think, it was big enough to sustain no fewer than eight punt-gunners, who supplied the local markets with duck, geese and anything else they thought was saleable. There were plenty of snipe too, but they were hard to get at because it was too wet. In those days they reckoned that six to fifteen couple counted as a good day's snipe shooting, nowadays we would class that as a bonanza! In 1851, the local landowners got together and with the assistance of drainage engineers and a new steam pumping engine, succeeded in draining the Mere. It was turned into grade A agricultural land that has been farmed ever since. The nearest habitats we have got to the old fen are places like Wicken Fen, Woodwalton Fen and the washlands... Oh! I am sorry, Alec was right, I have been rambling on!"

"No," said Tom. "I enjoyed hearing about it. I would've loved to have gone duck shooting on the Mere."

"You and me both Tom, you and me both," I agreed. "What an experience that would have been."

Alec had heard it all before and sat leaning back in his chair while tapping his glass on the table.

"And now young Tom," he grinned, "For asking him questions that set him off like that, you can now go to the bar and get this glass refilled. It's your round bor!"

20

November 18

At nine o'clock in the morning we collected Tom on our way to the farm belonging to his uncle George. A morning's shooting had been arranged for some friends and we were invited. When we turned into the farmyard there were already several vehicles parked and a motley crew standing around, the air thick with laughter and banter. An assortment of dogs ran around sniffing at each other, urinating against the nearest available car wheel and generally sorting out their own private pecking order. Most of the men were farming friends and neighbours of George, but among them I spotted Leonard, the local grocer who shot had with us in September and he walked across the yard to join us.

Alec introduced me to several members of the shooting party, and then pointed out a big old steam engine in an implement shed in the farmyard. I went for a closer look and found that there was more threshing tackle in the building. As a child I had seen steam traction engines working on the farm where my grandparents lived, but I had never seen an engine like this except in pictures. Unable to move under it's own power, this machine had to be towed into position and was in effect, an enormous stationary engine. The boiler was perhaps twelve feet long with a hinged funnel, which lying horizontally as it was, looked to be about the same length as the boiler. Standing upright in its working position, the funnel would make the engine look very much like Stephenson's 'Rocket'. Built by Marshalls of Gainsborough in 1908, the whole engine was rusty, but I was assured by the owner that the boiler was sound and when he had renovated the old girl, he intended to fire her up. I was still looking at this fascinating machine when George called us to order.

After reminding everyone that foxes were not to be shot because the farm was part of the local hunt country, George sorted everyone into groups of walking and standing guns. Alec was loaned a Land Rover to transport six of us to our stands, which were strung out behind a hedge that bordering a farm track. Together with an elderly gentleman called Geoffrey, I was stationed at the very end of the line. Alec then took the Land Rover across the fields behind us and parked to stand behind a wood. He would be back gun, to prevent any game going out of the far end. Before he went he said.

"When the walking guns get to the hedge you and Geoffrey head down to find me, the rest will go the other way round the wood."

Standing behind the low hedge I took in my surroundings. It was a bright day with a strong wind blowing and visibility was good. Before me stretched a fifty acre field of rape with, another hedge at the far end, beyond which could be seen a clutter of farm buildings. I should think we had been standing there for fifteen minutes when a vehicle appeared through a gap in the hedge, on the right-hand side of the rape field. Three guns jumped down, one stayed put and the others with their dogs walked away along the headland. A further ten minutes passed and then came the sound of a distant shot. A movement caught my eye and a small figure with a dog came into focus, then a second figure followed by a slowly moving 4x4 vehicle, which trundled down an incline from the buildings. Steadily the walking guns advanced into the rape and another shot was fired. Then a speeding shape crossed the hedge forty yards to my right. Hell! It was a partridge and almost gone by. My hurried shot did not even make it swerve. I could see that one of the walking guns was carrying a pheasant, which was just as well because nothing else was flushed from the field apart from another solitary partridge, and Geoffrey missed that.

Following Alec's instructions, Geoffrey and I walked down the side of the wood to find him. I noticed that the fingers of my companion's left hand were deformed by arthritis. He told me that this minor disability had obliged him to retire early from farming, but had not prevented him from handing his gun. When we foregathered, Alec suggested that I go over a bridge and stand about thirty yards into a meadow and forty back from the wood. He and Geoffrey were covering the side in case any birds broke out. I took up my position as the other guns were streaming in from the far end. The wood was perhaps thirty acres in extent, and it seemed we could hear the walking guns beating through it for a very long time. For all their efforts not many birds came forward. Of the six guns in the line only the two at the far end had any shooting, and they missed all but one of the half-a-dozen pheasants that went over them. Two or three birds broke back resulting in shots resounding through the trees. Two more went out of the side, where Alec missed and Geoffrey scored.

For the third and final drive we were taken up a hill to stand behind a wood. I was placed where the taller trees ended and the covert continued, as low scrub behind a short thick hedge. Alec was sixty yards to my right and two other stood guns beyond him, out of sight. Again the walking guns worked their way through a large area of roots and although I could not see them, I could hear an occasional shot. As the guns came nearer so the pigeons left the wood. Then a pair of magpies darted about, going nowhere in particular, until Alec knocked one down. The other bird fled, chattering abuse as it swerved over a hedge. Eventually another gun appeared at the far end of the low cover and stood out in the rape parallel to me. The sound of voices, tapping and shouts came closer; the clatter of a rising pheasant followed by a shot indicated that some action was in the offing. Then some birds flew out at Alec's corner of the wood. To my left I could see clearly, with everything lit by the low bright sun. I saw perfectly well when three pheasants crept through the hedge and took wing, but they were seventy yards away. A sound from in front heralded a hen bird, approaching at speed. My best chance of the morning, and I blew it! I turned for a second shot, but was blinded by the sun so didn't fire. The same thing happened when two birds came low out of the wood on my right. I did try a shot, but the birds flew on. I saw Alec drop two single birds, the chap on the end missed one that came out over him and then it was all over. Thank goodness Alec was on the ball, he killed five pheasants and a magpie on that drive and that turned out to be more than half the total bag.

When the twenty of us sat down to lunch in the pub, there was some analysis of the morning, and I discovered that the average bag was four times today's ten pheasants. It didn't matter, for this was not a commercial shoot where the keeper would face a reprimand if the guns didn't get their five hundred birds - this was a gathering of countrymen simply enjoying some open-air fun in their own backyard. Cheers and laughter greeted George when he summed up the morning.

"There were a few birds about," he said. "It was just that you lot weren't up to the bloody job!"

He was not far wrong, but let there be no doubt that, to a man, we were up to the task of devouring the great slabs of steak and kidney pie that were laid before us.

We had intended to try again for duck that evening, but it was half past three before we left the pub and in truth I was not sorry when Alec suggested we give it a miss.

21

November 24

Some weeks ago, Alec had talked of an uncle of his who resided somewhere in the backwoods of Galloway and Dumfries. When they had recently been spoken on the telephone, the uncle had suggested that Alec went up to stay for a couple of days shooting.

"Bring a friend if you like," the older man had kindly added. "And dinnae be too long making up your mind about it now, we'll no be here for ever y'know."

"To hear him talk anyone would think he was about to pop off at any moment, but you wait 'til you see him!" Alec smiled.

I vaguely recalled Alec mentioning before that he had an uncle in Scotland, but quite where and how he lived I had no idea. However, it would not long before the answer to both of those questions was answered. We had arranged to drive up on the Friday and make the return journey on the Sunday, and now incredibly the Friday was upon us. Our guns, cartridges, clothes, spare clothes and other shooting paraphernalia were piled into the back of the car. We double checked everything for it would be extremely irritating to travel so far from home only to realise that a vital piece of equipment had been carelessly left behind. Two items we weren't taking were the dogs. Uncle Alan had assured us that we would not need them, besides which he wanted to work his own pair of retrievers. I did my best to prevent Jet from seeing our preparations, but my efforts were only partially successful and it was difficult to resist those large brown, pleading eyes when the time came to leave.

Three-quarters of an hour later we had joined the Great North Road and settled down as the seemingly everlasting grey ribbon unwound before our eyes. We slowly ticked off landmarks and aimed for the next, until we eventually crossed the border. I mentioned to Alec that I had read somewhere of a group of wildfowlers who made the annual pilgrimage in search of the Solway geese, and every year as they crossed the border there was a chorus of "Och Aye!" Alec agreed.

"I'm not certain, but I think that was possibly BB, then again I might be wrong."

Not so far north of Castle Douglas my friend began to study our surroundings carefully. It was he explained several years since he had visited his relatives.

"Ah!" He exclaimed, with very little warning. "Turn in this gate near the tree."

I duly turned, quickly to find that we were on a gravelled road, climbing a gentle slope. After a while the road curved in a wide bend in front of a large, solid looking, stone-built farmhouse behind which the land rose dramatically. In front of the house the land sloped away gradually until, at the far side of a sheep-cropped valley, it swept up again into low hills. There was the sound of furious barking before a pair of border collies appeared from a corner of the yard and tore towards us like coursing greyhounds that had just been slipped. Neck and neck they ran, overshot and skidded on the gravel in an attempt to be first to turn. Then they chased the car until the point when we almost reached the yard. I say almost, because a figure emerged from a door at the back of the house, no doubt to see what was causing the din. The man waved an ash stick in the air and uttered a mighty roar, which instantly had the collies slinking back to their rightful station, and peace was restored.

"Come and meet Uncle Alan," said Alec.

I do not know how I had visualised this man in my mind's eye. A typical pensioner I suppose, but certainly not this rugged-faced, wiry individual who moved as easily as a man half his age. The introductions over, we shared a late lunch, which Alec's relatives having been advised of a rough estimate of our arrival time, had delayed especially for our benefit.

Over coffee I listened as Alec regaled his Uncle and Aunt with more family news and in return received some back from the Scottish branch of his tribe. It was akin to sitting in a registrar's office with the abundant details of births, deaths and marriages being exchanged. Aunt Harriet had just told us that wee Stewart had been walking and talking for some weeks now, when Alan turned to us.

"As you have only the one full day, might you like to try for a duck this evening?"

We assured him that there was nothing we would like better, so he suggested that we leave our bags upstairs and change into more suitable clothes. He added that he wanted to be making tracks by five o'clock at the latest. At ten to five we trooped outside and boarded a mud-spattered Land Rover - the only sort of Land Rover worth having. A brace of sleek and shining black labradors peered silently at us from the rear of the vehicle. Obedient though they were, they could not prevent the thump of their tails expressing their joy at being included, wherever we were headed.

We drove steadily through woods, hills and fells, climbing all the time. The vehicle seemed always to have its bonnet several degrees above horizontal. Parking amongst pine trees we disembarked and walked the last half-mile, and still heading upwards. As I commented to Alec, being used to finding our duck in the lowest ground it seemed strange to go in search of them so high up.

"Wait and see!" was the only reply I got out of him.

Suddenly, we emerged from the trees and a lovely scene opened up before our eyes. We were on the flat summit of our hill, but others rose around and above it. Time was getting on so Uncle Alan showed us to the positions he wanted us to occupy for the flight. Once we were stationed, he repeated his instructions to allow the first lot of duck to come in. With that he retreated, labradors at heel, to some thick cover two hundred yards behind and between us.

Now I had time to take stock of what really was a beautiful setting. In front and to my left were hills, which loomed blue in the dying light. A burn came in from the left. It spread wide through this boggy top creating a pond, or lochan. The burn might have been dammed to cause the widening or it might have just been natural, as ancient lochans often are. I would have to ask later. It spread over one hundred yards down to where I knew Alec was hidden after which the burn carried on meandering through the trees, fir on one side, Scots pine on the other. What a painting such a scene could have inspired.

Dusk stole upon us like a thief in the night and with it, almost at once, the first team of duck. We dutifully watched them pitch in but, duty done, gripped our guns in readiness.

Patience was not tested, for in no time at all the next lot came sailing in. They appeared to be following the burn and showed suddenly as they came out of the dark backdrop of trees. Over Alec came a dozen chuckling mallard and two of their number fell to a cracking right and left. The survivors flared and scattered. One of them came hurrying past me silhouetted nicely against the western sky, he too folded and dropped. In the half an hour that followed I killed two more, while Alec had four down. The fourth of these had been a very high bird, which sent up a tremendous plume of water when it crashed into the lochan. After my last one it was almost too dark to see, so I stood up intending to collect it, as it had fallen not far away. However, I heard a rustling in the cover and one of Alan's dogs appeared with the bird in his soft mouth.

Alan loomed up out of the gloom and with the aid of his retrievers, gathered the duck from the pond. He seemed suitably impressed that we had killed nine mallard and not one had fallen further than fifty yards from the water's edge. It turned out that he had previously entertained guests who claimed rather disingenuously, birds down a quarter of a mile away. Of course he had felt duty-bound to attempt a search, even though in his heart of hearts he knew it would be futile - only the guests pride had actually been hit. Tonight was definitely not one of those nights and it was a happy band that descended the hill to the welcoming warmth of the farmhouse.

22

November 25

Nine-thirty, a nice civilized hour to start on a Saturday morning, and just as well after a session at Uncle Alan's whisky. While we relaxed after supper the previous evening, with generous measures in our glasses, I had learned a little more about the farming life that Alan and Harriet led up here with the help of their son, Malcolm. They owned and rented quite a large acreage of land, but much of it was not very productive even for a livestock farmer. The farm was a mixture of rough pasture, hills, vales, bogs and bracken. They ran some hardy cattle on the lower ground and several hundred sheep over parts of the remainder, but now to help balance the books they were experimenting by letting a day's rough shooting now and then throughout the shooting season. There was a reasonable stock of wild pheasants, which attracted wandering birds from a nearby estate. Alan told us that the trial had worked well for the first time last season, and they had come to an arrangement with the landlords of a local inn who had been only too pleased to accommodate sportsmen travelling from a distance. Alec added that if the venture took off they would have to consider putting some reared birds down.

Now we stood at the front of the house as a fine drizzle tried, but failed to dampen our enthusiasm. Malcolm arrived shortly after completing some early morning chores. After he had a few words with his father, the four of us set off down a shining wet track alongside a stone wall. The weather did not bother us as we were all wearing protective coats and leggings. In addition, instead of my usual cap I had donned a tweed trilby so that the water ran off on all sides. Malcolm and Alan insisted from the start that they would carry our game and that they would not use bags. As we clumped ever downward along the track they also pointed out that Alan would walk with Alec while I would be accompanied by Malcolm, and that where possible we would try to give each other driven shots. The theory actually worked on occasion. For example we had left the track and were walking down a slope with the farm's boundary, a tree-lined gully to our left. Alec and Alan were walking a parallel line eighty yards away and several feet above us. One after another they flushed three single pheasants, and each one of them flew like stink for the boundary. One after another I killed them, wings snapped shut, heads flung back, well-shot birds. Alec told me later that as the third bird fell, Alan had muttered - "Yon friend o' yours is a fine shot." It must have been the kiss of death for I proceeded to miss the next three and Alan made no further comment.

It rained on and off all day as we climbed and descended, scrambled up rugged slopes and pushed through high and soaking bracken. As we came over the brow of one hill, more than a hundred greylag geese lumbered noisily from a small loch below us. We watched as they sorted themselves out into a long line that came together and then strung out again, as they disappeared into the mist and murk at the base of a distant hill. Even on this day of poor visibility, the surroundings were beautiful and I mentally thanked Alec for including me on this trip. Pheasants were flushed below us, in front of us, behind us and above us. Birds rose singly or in threes and fours and once, as we walked cautiously on either side of a large reedy bog, the retrievers vanished and moments later with a terrific clatter eight, ten, no twelve pheasants erupted from the reeds. Three of these were added to the neat, feathered bundles hanging from the sticks of our hosts.

Lunch was taken in a stone-built building adjacent to a cattle byre. We sat on wooden crates covered with sacks, and started on our flasks of hot soup with bread, cheese and an onion. When we were into the coffee and put matches to tobacco, our hosts told us of other days they had enjoyed on the hill. Malcolm had never been down as far as the fens, but he mentioned that he had read somewhere that someone had once shot a huge number of snipe with a puntgun. I said that I thought he must have read the account in James Wentworth Day's 'A History of the fens' when a fenman set up a puntgun to cover an area of marshy ground near Whittlesey Mere. He was reported to have killed an incredible thirty-six dozen snipe with one shot.

Spookily, the first bird I shot at after lunch was a snipe, but this one was in luck for I missed it. We carried on, walking in and out of showers for another hour-and-a-half until Alec and I were positioned seventy yards apart halfway down a slope, while Alan and Malcolm headed away and then round a knoll. When the pair reappeared they were climbing steadily upwards, at least a hundred feet above us. The plan was that they would attempt to drive any game they found out over our guns. When you translate a hundred feet into yards it is only thirty-three, but I can assure you that for most sportsmen they would be deemed high birds. Unfortunately our little strategy did not quite go to plan. Our 'beaters' had got around the birds too efficiently. Pheasants began to flush from the top of the hill all right, flushing very well too. One goes, a pause of a few seconds, there goes another, but they were going out at an angle so that they passed a hundred yards to our right. I wondered if I should move to get under them as another three followed the leaders. I decided to stay put as our hosts had placed me and it would have been most embarrassing to have moved, only to have birds go over the spot I had vacated. I was right to stand my ground, for the last few birds did come more kindly. Three singletons sailed down the slope on set wings, going like the clappers. Alec killed the last cock bird with a cracking shot just before Alan and Malcolm appeared on the skyline.

When they had descended, we gave them time to catch their breath before heading back towards the distant farmhouse. The dogs worked away as though they had just begun rather than finished the day, and I envied them their energy. The land sloped away down and still down, to level out near a sheep fence beyond which, lay a tussock-covered bog. I happened to be looking that way when a pheasant was flushed by one of the labradors. It was strange to be shooting downhill, but I was getting the hang of it after this terrific day of shooting at all angles. The bird was over forty yards away when I fired and when it faltered and then flew on I wished I had not pulled the trigger. Thankfully however, it suddenly fell backwards, tumbling over and over until it came to earth just beyond the fence. Malcolm was scrambling down the slope with the dogs ahead of him. One of them took the fence at a gallop and cleared it as gracefully as a deer, what a grand sight. After casting around for less than a minute, down went his head and up it came with the bird in mouth. Just to show off, he trotted back to the fence and before Malcolm could assist him, bounded over once again!

By the time the farmhouse hove into view we were all pretty weary and beginning to realise how wet we were. Although, in deference to the manufacturers of waxed waterproofs, I have to say that most of it was perspiration. The birds were braced up and hung in a barn and we found that the bag was nineteen. We took our guns apart and dried them as best we could and then left them on an old blanket until we could attend to them again later. Good old Harriet, knowing the condition we would be in on our return, had plenty of scalding hot water available for welcome baths.

We were sitting pink-faced in the warm kitchen, and I suppose feeling pretty smug with ourselves, when Alan came down from his bath. He looked over at us.

"Dinnae be making ye'selves too comfortable, we're off after the duck in an hour!" He laughed at our expressions adding. "Not to worry, we'll be driving most of the way, unless of course you've had enough for one day and would rather not go oot in the nasty rain again?"

He hooted even more at our spluttered replies, which would have been even more colourful had not Harriet been present.

"An hour it is then," he grinned, as he took up his position in an ancient oak armchair. After tapping out his blackened briar, he refilled it from his pouch, twisted a spill from a piece of newspaper, lit up from the fire and leaned back contentedly, wreathed in clouds of pungent blue smoke.

Shortly afterwards Alec and I went to rub over our guns with a lightly oiled cloth before reassembling them. Then we sorted out some more clothes. Wordlessly making sure no one could accuse us of hanging back when the time came to go out again. We would be ready! Alan would have chuckled had he seen us, but he was still drawing on his pipe when we returned, almost guiltily to the kitchen.

The hour had come, and out we went to join Malcolm in the old Land Rover. It was a bit cramped tonight with the four of us, plus two steaming labradors. At least the showers seemed to have blown over, but needless to say that by the end of the journey the interior of that motor smelt decidedly 'doggy.' We did not return to the previous night's lochan, moving instead into more open country where there were very few trees. It was still rugged and hilly though and the Land Rover was at times leaning at some pretty crazy angles. This was the stuff for which the vehicle was designed of course, and it made nothing of it. Eventually, we lurched to a stop near a stunted thorn-bush and disembarked. Alan led the way through a gate that looked as though it might suddenly fall to pieces at the slightest touch of a careless hand or a mere breath of a breeze, but of course it didn't. Having stood the test of time, and all the elements that had been thrown at these wild hills, the gate would doubtless hang there for a long time to come. We followed Alan across a patch of very rough ground then down a slope to a small hillock. We were suddenly presented with a dramatic view. Just below us was a reed-fringed lochan, perhaps two acres in size. There was a small kidney shaped island a third of the way along its length. Beyond the water, the rough land rolled away to the foot of a low hill on the western horizon.

"Same procedure as last night lads," came Alan's instructions. "Let the first lot come in and leave the picking-up to me."

With that, he led Alec round to the far side of the pond while I stayed with Malcolm.

139

"This is usually a teal pond, but you can never guarantee they'll come." Malcolm observed. "They're here today, gone tomorrow. There were forty or fifty coming in here last week so be on your guard. I'm moving back a bit, out of your way but I'll mark down your birds, you just concentrate on shooting! Good luck"

As Malcolm crept away, I checked safety angles and speculated as to the direction from which the duck might come. It was a lovely evening with a pale grey sky, but no wind. Whether or not a good wind would have made any difference we shall never know, but only a few mallard showed up at dusk. Ironically, the first pair to come presented my best chance. They came in high and dropped in on cupped wings right over my head. I steadfastly held my fire and watched as they planed into the far end of the pond, shook their feathers into place and swam into the shadows. The next one to arrive seemed as though it would land on Alec's head and it pitched just out from his hiding place. Surely he must have seen it? Then I realised that he and Alan might be looking towards the lighter sky away from the pond. Wings... Where the...? Ah yes, a pair of black shapes now in a light patch of sky. Booom! The shot sounded remarkably loud, echoing around and off the hill. The leading black shape blurred and arched down to shatter the still surface of the pond with an splendid splash. Another shot rang out from Alec's gun. It transpired that following my shot, the duck that had pitched near them departed in a hurry, right over the backs of their heads. Alec had recovered quickly enough to drop it before it had covered thirty yards. We missed another couple and that was the end of the flight. As we walked back to the Land Rover, Alan attempted to apologise for the lack of birds. We assured him that this was not necessary. As wildfowlers we knew all about the uncertainties of the game, indeed that was part of the mystery and charm of the sport. On the coast or inland, these were wild birds, free to come and go as they pleased. We wouldn't have it any other way.

The Land Rover bumped and rolled like a destroyer in a heavy sea, but she brought us safely back to port. Relaxed and changed, we took on supper and yet another session at Uncle Alan's seemingly endless supply of Aberlour single malt whisky. Be sure, we slept soundly that night and I for one dreamt of pheasants sailing off a high hillside and mallard coming on flickering wings to hidden hill lochs.

In the morning, after an enormous breakfast of grilled bacon, chops, eggs and sausages laid on by the inimitable Aunt Harriet, we loaded up the car and made ready to depart. Alan would accept none of our birds insisting that he had a brace hanging already, so we gladly found room for the nineteen pheasants and eleven mallard we had gathered during this fantastic forty-eight hours. It was with some reluctance that we bid Alec's relatives farewell and set out on the long trek south.

23

December 1

The moon in the first quarter and waxing towards full, had been producing enough light during the past two evenings to encourage us to try a flight. Alec had turned up late in the afternoon and as the moon rises early during this phase, we wasted no time, setting out at once on the short drive to the washes. The sun was already sinking steadily to the horizon as we left the car. I had parked on the grass near a low bridge spanning a slow moving, twenty-five foot wide waterway. After climbing over a five-barred gate, which for some reason was chained and locked, we proceeded a short distance by the drain-side before striking off at ninety degrees along a grass drove between two dykes that were brimful with water. The cattle marshes stretched away on all sides, bleak and deserted now that the livestock had all been shipped off to spend the winter in the strawed-up crew yards. The isolation and emptiness adds to the attraction as far as the wildfowler is concerned, and indeed for the wildfowl. The very air felt damp and slightly misty. Puddles of water twinkled among the spiked tussocks, occasionally linking up to spread into larger pools. The place all but spoke of snipe and I told Alec of one evening at dusk when I knelt among these same tussocks, as the long-bills flew, in showing in sharp focus against a pink frosty sky. They had come singly for the most part, with occasionally pairs and trios. I had experienced some marvellous sport for a quarter of an hour, collecting six snipe.

Tonight, however, we were hoping for wigeon and therefore purposely left behind this inviting little marsh, walking onwards along the grass drove. I had just advised Alec to remain on the alert, as it was not unusual to flush a stray pheasant from the cover at the side of the drove or even teal from the dyke, when a harsh quacking caused us both to look up. A pair of mallard, droplets of water still dripping from their webbed orange feet, had sprung from the dyke just sixty yards ahead. In seconds they had put another ten yards between us, making a shot out of the question.

"Hell! I was just saying…" I started.

Jet looked at me as if wondering why I had not fired. A combination of things had spoiled what might have been a chance of a bonus duck. The water level in the dyke was higher than usual, and this twinned with the fact that we were walking side by side did not help. We had been visible from some distance.

"In September or October you would have walked right onto them." I mused, watching the progress of the mallard far across the washes and out over the river until, minute specks, they turned into the wind and slowly descended to the farmland beyond the riverbank.

"Ah well," I continued. "They've gone in to feed slightly earlier tonight. I wonder what's on the menu?"

"Rotting potatoes I shouldn't wonder," laughed Alec.

At the end of the drove we entered a string of marshes upon which could be seen sizeable flashes of surface water that glittered with the light of the ever-lowering sun. I was hoping that recent rain had freshened the pools, restoring their attractiveness to the local wild duck. We walked along the eastern edge of the largest flash, taking up positions eighty yards apart so that we could look over the water to the western horizon. As we had half-expected, nothing much moved at the last light of dusk, except travelling lapwings that flew so low that they passed between us even though we were kneeling. I looked round sharply as an unmistakable clatter of wings from the riverbank heralded the approach of a pheasant.

Alec's shouted warning was unnecessary - I had heard the bird for myself. When I did see it, it was too late. Gliding low, I glimpsed him for only a fraction of a second. Even in silhouette there could be no doubt that he was a cock bird. Jet sat quivering with excitement, his ears cocked and his muzzle following the line taken by the disappearing bird. The pheasant was making for his bed in some dry, sheltered patch of rushes out in the washes where he would be reasonably safe from the attention of foxes. He had most probably used the same spot for a while and would carry on using it until he was scared off, or became ill at ease, feeling an inner pressure to change his habits. He would not have the brain to work this out, but more often than not his natural survival instinct would keep him safe.

It was dark now so we moved to the other side of the water to face the moon, which had risen well before dusk and was now high up in the sky looking like a letter D with a beer gut. As usual the wind was from the southwest, which gave us a slight advantage in that any duck intending to alight on our water would come in with the light of the moon behind.

There was some light cloud scattered around the sky and things began to look promising. I suppose it must have been three quarters of an hour later that I heard the first wigeon approaching, a burst of excited whistling and then silence apart from an occasional call. They went speeding along the middle of the washes, unseen by either of us. Another larger company following on the same line. This bunch was equally invisible, but their route could be guessed from the rushing sound of air disturbed by those hurrying wings. No more than half a minute passed before we heard the pop, pop, popop...pop. of distant gunfire. It seemed that the wigeon had headed for flashes further down the washes and had found some of the local gunners lying in wait. It was not long before the whole lot returned the way they had come, more vocal and flying faster than before. They gave our flashes not even a glance. Instead they disappeared in an easterly direction, protesting to all and sundry as they went. All this we surmised from what we heard, for we saw not a bird.

The clouds then vanished, leaving the moon naked and exposed, and us with a sky that was impossible to shoot by. We could only wait and hope for more cloud to arrive. I splashed my way over to Alec.

"Fancy a stretch?" I enquired. After the cramped position of kneeling it was a relief to stand erect and move around a bit. Together we walked the short distance to the field gate with its sturdy posts and rails, where we leaned on the top rail of the gate and prayed for clouds. It wasn't long before Alec was packing his pipe with 'Exmoor Hunt' broad-cut mixture, so I followed his example and there we stood making a good attempt at creating our own personal clouds. The trouble with our clouds was they had no substance and they drifted off to rapidly disperse.

A small pack of wigeon returned, following the same route as the earlier party. Unsurprisingly, no shots greeted them this time and I could imagine the gunners cursing the lack of cloud as they stared ineffectually into the velvet void. The wigeon must have found a safe haven for we heard no more from them.

"What do you think, are we going to get any more cloud?" I asked Alec.

"Let's give it another hour." he suggested.

So we went back to our chosen spots amid the tussocks. Some time later the cloud did drift up on the wind, but it was not the type we had hoped for. Rather than fluffy white beauties, a whole bank of heavy thick stuff stifled the sky. Where the lunar light broke through there was a lighter patch, but the moon was now surrounded by a close fitting halo of light, a sure indication of rain to come.

I knelt there contemplating this change in circumstances, as my eyes wandered along the place where the lowering cloud met the far edge of the water. Even as I watched, a dim but familiar shape appeared with at least one other and it braked to land. I flung up the gun and fired as it touched my shoulder. I saw no more, but I heard a splash and so did Jet for he had already bounded off to retrieve. I was puzzled because I thought I had identified a mallard, but the mallard should all be out on the fields. I speculated that perhaps this bunch had come to wash the mud from their feet. They often feel the need to do this because a certain type of mud builds up on a duck's paddles just as it will on our boots. In our case we feel six inches taller until the mud falls or we shake it off. Imagine my surprise when I saw Jet trotting back with a goose in his mouth. When I inspected it, I found that it was a whitefronted goose. This made sense, as of all the local geese; the whitefront is a species that prefers a diet of grass

146

above all else. What I had taken for a mallard at a reasonable range had in fact been a goose at long range. However, this little goose wasn't much bigger than a good old drake mallard so the confusion was understandable in that light. Anyway, it was legal quarry and an unexpected bonus. The inferences of absolute jam, uttered by Alec at regular intervals all the way home, went totally unheeded by me. I let them drift away like pipe-smoke on the wind.

Those impenetrable clouds were still with us in the morning, but now they had opened the taps to give our immediate world a distinctly soggy appearance. That halo around the moon had been an accurate forecaster and using one of the old rural rhymes, I made my own forecast.

"Rain before seven, fine by eleven."

"That's what they say," agreed Alec, "and that's usually right." And so it was on this day: by noon the thick blanket of cloud had moved on to be replaced by a thinner, more scattered variety. We decided to take advantage of the dry spell and went to Jack's farm in search of game. The farmer was in one of the buildings in his yard making some minor repairs to his potato harvester that had completed its work for another year. He greeted us amiably and had a moan about the weather.

"We shall be getting the last of the beet up next week all being well, so if you want to try in there this'll be your last chance this season," he added.

We thanked him and enquired as to whether he would like a bird if we were successful.

"No, we can't be doing with one this near to Christmas. We've got several cockerels to get ready for people and they'll keep us busy enough, but thanks all the same. And anyway," he laughed, "If you're going to mauter through that there beet, you deserve any birds you get!" We laughed too, before leaving him to his repair job.

Although the rain had ceased, the leaves of the sugar beet were absolutely full of water and the black soil squelched soddenly, beneath our boots.

"We won't find many pheasants or anything else in this lot you know," opined Alec and I had to admit I was inclined to agree with him. Nevertheless, we ploughed stubbornly on until the point was proven. The only birds we saw were two separate cock pheasants that flew up from the headlands three hundred yards ahead of us, and did they fly? They climbed rapidly and sped away across the fen, their long tails streaming in their wake, as high as any 'high pheasant' on hillier terrain.

"Wild as hawks." came the muttered comment from my companion.

"Good birds though." Said I, in defence of the fen pheasant.

"They would be if we were under them," came the ready retort. We walked the dykes, flushing only two more birds, one of which was within shot and was added to the bag. The only other bird we bagged was a hen bird that burst up from a deep furrow in the ploughed land we were crossing to get back to the car. Both of our birds were wet and bedraggled and it all felt in some measure not quite the thing.

It was half-past-three when we arrived back at the house. There was time for a quick sandwich before changing into duck shooting gear. Instead of trying the washes again we decided to investigate whether any duck were leaving the river to fly into or at least, over Chris's farm. With this plan in mind, we turned up near the old barn about forty minutes before dusk and hurried along a farm track to a field of winter wheat adjacent to the drain, which ran parallel to the river. A dry dyke ran down one headland of the wheat field and at right angles to the drain. It was barely three feet deep, but provided ample cover for a crouching gunner. The moon would be up by now, but that damned cloud had returned and right on dusk it began to drizzle again.

All was not lost though, for I could see one or two mallard flying in to feed on the small potatoes, which remained on the field between the neat green rows of wheat. I called one pair right over me and then for some inexplicable reason missed them both clean. I heard Alec shooting at the same time and saw him scramble out of the dyke and walk across the drills to retrieve something, that I guessed was a mallard. My companion had only just got back down into the dyke when a pack of wigeon scorched over my head from behind me, gliding in on cupped wings straight along the dyke. It was too late for me to shoot, but I shouted a warning to Alec who responded with both barrels. It so happened that another party of wigeon was following close behind and they flared back over me at the sound of the shots, allowing me the chance to bring one down. I reloaded as Jet bolted out to fetch my duck. I was watching him trot back, tail wagging, when low across the field sped a dozen or more wigeon. They showed up sharp and black against the last of the light. I am certain they did not see me, but as they came into range they bunched and at that moment I squeezed the trigger. It seemed to rain wigeon and I was so taken aback that I forgot to fire again. Three duck had fallen to the shot and Jet was happily collecting them. Following this storm came the calm and soon silence reigned. Placing the birds into my game bag I made my way to Alec. He had four duck in the dyke with him and another out on the field. He indicated where he thought it had dropped and I sent Jet out. He was back with the bird, another wigeon within thirty seconds. Good old Jet.

149

The rain came on in earnest as we plodded back to the old barn and the car, but with eight wigeon and the mallard safely tucked into our bags the weather could do what it jolly well liked.

24

December 8

It was in the middle of the week that Alec telephoned to suggest a tide flight on his bit of the North Norfolk coast. With a voice brimming with enthusiasm, he said.

"The moon is just on the wane, the spring tides are still getting well into the saltings and high water on Friday is at about twenty to ten, which is just about perfect. Thing is, I haven't been down there for a while and have become a bit rusty with the local knowledge so I have asked old Frank, he's a local crab fisherman, if he will take us out. If you can possibly get over to my place on Thursday afternoon, we can make an early start in the morning."

From a shooting perspective, this part of the coast was new to me, and it is always interesting to shoot in unfamiliar surroundings. I suppose the interest is due largely to the excitement and anticipation of the unknown. Whatever, I made sure I kept the dates free and found I could hardly contain my impatience for the weekend to roll round again. Eventually the days passed and Thursday found me making tracks towards that quiet unpretentious hospitality from Alec and Molly I had come to value so much.

As usual it was good old Rosy with that ever-wagging tail who was first to greet me on my arrival at the cottage. I gave her head a rub as she waddled beside me towards the back porch. Molly had heard the car and met me at the door with a smile.

"He's down with the birds if you want to go and find him. Tell him the tea's brewing, that'll get him back up here if anything will."

I grinned in agreement and turned back past the chicken house. My gun-damaged sense of hearing picked up soft murmurings emanating from the fusty interior of the wooden hut. I continued along the path through the vegetable garden. Save for a few lonely looking sticks of sprouts it was all dug over for the winter. Alec saw me coming as I weaved my way through the now leafless fruit trees and raised a hand in greeting. In his other hand was a plastic bucket half full of wheat, which he was feeding to his ducks. Six mallard greedily guzzled at the corn, but I noticed the solitary wigeon slink off into the redundant hen house in which they were shut up for the night.

"He's still shy after all this time," my friend smiled. "But I like him that way - he retains some of his wildness. Not like these blighters." Alec waved a hand towards the mallards. "They would eat out of any hand that offered them food and they're not that particular what food it is either!"

With that, he emptied the remains of the wheat into a long galvanised trough and we strolled back to the cottage and joined Molly in the kitchen.

At half-past-four the next morning, the old Ford Popular rumbled out of the shadowy yard and we spent the next thirty minutes or so trying to catch up with our headlights along those narrow hedged-in roads between the cottage and the coast. Rabbits dodged across the road and once a hare, caught in the beam and not knowing which way to turn, loped along the centre of the road ahead of us. It finally bounded off onto the verge and away. We had come over the high ground ridge and were dropping down to the coast road, which we travelled along until we came to the village that was our destination. Driving through the narrow streets of the sleeping village, Alec turned off the quayside onto a gravely hard and parked where we wouldn't be in anyone's way. Our footsteps sounded unnaturally loud in the still quietness of the early morning as we made our way down to the quay. Fishing boats and ferryboats tugged at their moorings in the darkness, thumping softly against the fenders of neighbouring vessels. At least, on such a windless morning we were spared the usual ceaseless rattle of halyards whipping against the metal masts of the massed ranks of sailing dinghies.

In our enthusiasm we had turned up early so, while we waited for Frank we stood on the hard where it sloped down to the channel, listening for sounds of wildfowl on the move. The searching beam of headlamps swept round a bend on the coast road and a few moments later a battered pick-up truck turned into the hard, and crunched over the gravel, drawing to a standstill next to the Ford. The truck reeked of diesel oil, fish, salt and the sea. A brace of crab pots rattled about in the back, taken home for minor repairs no doubt. The driver's door swung open and out stepped a burly figure wearing thigh boots. Alec introduced us. Frank was good-natured fellow, with a ready wit and an undying enthusiasm for wildfowl and wildfowling that matched our own. He beamed at us as he briefed us with his plans for the morning. A few moments later we were striding off to put those same plans into action.

Our walk was easy as the waning moon, now high in the sky, lit our way most generously. Only the soft thud of our footsteps and the occasional rustle of clothing broke the silence. We left the grassy bank we had been walking along and dipped down onto a narrow strip of marsh, until we came to the brink of a fairly wide channel. Frank lowered himself down into the channel and began to wade across. Following his lead, we found the bottom to be sand, firm and hard. The water lapped just above our knees and although each step was taken cautiously, there were no hidden holes or deeper places, just a nice constant depth. We clambered out on the far side to find ourselves on close-cropped grass. After a short walk across this, we sloped down again onto a wide stretch of sand, the surface patterned with the serried ranks of wave-like forms. Although they are a familiar sight at the seaside I am nevertheless, always fascinated by these wonderful formations of sand wavelets, which are one of nature's oft repeated minor miracles.

Soundlessly now, we moved like ghosts across the sands that reached palely ahead until merging into the darkness. I looked up at the sky, which was like black velvet shot with pinpricks of stars that winked and blinked as brightly as any diamond, yet it was not in the least cold. We were, of course, being kept warm by our exertions, but the air lacked that bite that one would normally expect with so clear a sky. True, there were occasional wisps of white cloud that came drifting across, but no great banks of the heavy stuff. It was just as one of these patches was sailing above us that the clamour of geese stopped us all in our tracks. As they grew nearer, the rolling, cronking calls readily identified them as brent and presently they appeared, or at least half appeared.

154

A ragged pack lumbered overhead, vaguely glimpsed, then a few of them momentarily showed jet black against the thin layer of cloud. There was the sound of strong pinions and a crescendo of goose voices when they were directly overhead, which faded quickly as the skein beat farther out towards the estuary. What did it matter if since 1954, brent were no longer a quarry species, even if we had been able to see them properly? That brief interlude was one of those magical moments that are part and parcel of wildfowling.

Resuming our trek over the wanly illuminated, rippled and seemingly endless sands, we plodded silently onwards, our footsteps muffled by the softness underfoot. Only when one or another of us splashed through one of the many shining pools left behind by the previous tide, could our presence have been detected. Then, almost without warning the sand petered out and we found ourselves on mud, which after a few more paces brought us onto saltings and the familiar network of creeks and gutters. If it were not cold before, now we became even warmer as we plunged up and down, in and out of obstacles for a further fifteen minutes before Frank called a halt. He pointed out a gutter in which he suggested Alec should hide, spending a moment or two advising my friend of the expected direction of the fowl. He then returned to me and led the way for a considerable distance taking me to my position for the flight.

"If you hide somewhere here, you'll be all right. There's a channel in front of you and when the tide starts to flood, the ol' wigeon sometimes fly along it. Don't worry about retrieving, just mark down what you get. I'll be between the two of you with the dog and will be able to see most of what goes on."

After these concise instructions, Frank moved off behind me, silent as his own marshes and was soon lost to sight in the all-enclosing gloom.

After Frank had gone, I went to inspect the channel. This was partly out of curiosity, but also to ascertain exactly how far it was from my proposed hiding place. I found that it was not far at all; In fact it was barely twenty-five yards. The channel was thirty, perhaps as much as forty feet wide with fairly steep sides and the water therein was - at the moment - some eight feet below the level of the marsh. Beyond the channel I could see the marsh edge and made a mental note that anything falling on the opposite bank to me would land on bare sand, which would be an advantage when it came to retrieving. Noticing that the tide was already creeping up the channel, I retreated to my gutter. I moved along it until I found as firm a footing as was possible in a muddy creek, before making sure I could swing the gun to cover a good wide frontage. Finally came a quick check of the barrels against the lightening sky. Finding them bright and clear of obstruction, I slipped a couple of Grand Prix number fives into the breech and leaned back on my bag to contemplate the coming of a brand new day.

Pale shades of greens, greys and yellows merged and spread, as the moon took on more of a back seat in the dawning process. Gulls, as ever, were the first of the avian tribes to make a move, angling across the mud on soft silent wings. A lone curlew flew past well beyond the channel, but nevertheless following its course. At first I thought it was another gull, but the quicker wing-beat caused me to look closer until the long bill could clearly be seen, then there was no doubt as to the bird's identity. It spotted me at the same moment, panicked, banked away and woke up the saltings with a raucous warning - kooorlew!

The sound of many more birds on the wing was sure indication that the flooding tide was making its presence felt. I watched intently now as anything could happen. Almost immediately it did - a fast moving party of little black dots had come into view. They may have appeared as mere dots, but any experienced wildfowler will know at once from the pattern they make in the sky, whether or not they are duck. These were certainly duck, but just as certainly they were not intending to come anywhere near me. My eyes followed the speeding little smudge as they hurried on to who knew where. I was still watching them when, with a sudden rush of wings a small team of wigeon hurtled along the channel. I cursed myself for missing the first chance of the morning, for in our sport that first opportunity so often turns out to be the only opportunity! Even as the thought crossed my mind the bump of a double shot rolled across the mud. Oh well, at least Alec was wide awake.

Eyes front! All at once, from nowhere it seemed, twenty wigeon appeared, each bird sharply defined against the dawn sky, see-sawing, wings cupped, air brakes on, intent on dropping into the channel. I selected two birds and coolly took a deliberate right and left. Both duck folded and fell just as they were meant to. There was a movement from the left and Frank's spaniel came bounding effortlessly across the marsh. She didn't need the pip of a whistle or frantic hand signals, this bitch knew her business and was best left to get on with it. There seemed to be no set flight-line and duck appeared from all points of the compass, several from behind and more often than not, from a temporarily unwatched direction. All the same we both had some real chances. Once, I was forewarned when a shot from Alec made me look his way. Seconds later a duck came into view, intent on putting as much distance between itself and Alec as fast as ever it could. Unfortunately for the bird, it flew straight over my head - a gift, which almost fell on top of me. It was close enough to reach out and pick up and as I did so, I noticed it had a longer and narrower bill than the expected wigeon. Holding it to the light, I could see that it was a female pintail.

It was not long after this minor surprise when a piercing whistle from Frank confirmed that the light and tide had overtaken us. It was time to move back to higher ground. Behind us loomed the great shingle bank that kept the North Sea in check. A low grey-white mist hovered above the marsh. The sand-hills peeped above it looking like islands and cliffs seen from a boat.

Now that their food was underwater, straggly lines of brent geese beat their way up into the harbour to sit out the tide. Alec had caught up with our guide but as I made my way to join them, I spotted a lone wigeon approaching. It was still four hundred yards away, but surely it would see us soon, sticking out like sore thumbs. Despite this thought, I squatted down because birds will sometimes fly over, eyes and minds set fair on the far horizon. Things closer to hand are often ignored, unless of course, they happen to move. So it proved in this case, I was able to swing up to fire and I am certain that the duck never saw a thing. It was the last shot of the morning. I joined the others to make our way to a grass-covered sandy point to wait for, what Frank described as our taxi. He had evidently arranged for one of his colleagues to come and collect us by boat.

Sprawling on the marram grass we swapped stories of other flights, while we inspected the bag. Chestnut heads of the cock wigeon were admired, with their creamy beige crowns. I noticed that the colour was already fading from the blue-grey bills. The dazzling white of their shoulders reminded me of a good tip, which I passed on to the others. It is a good plan to keep the wings of cock wigeon and attach them, by means of strong elastic bands, to one's mallard decoys. It is remarkable how well they show up in poor light and the wigeon, or other duck for that matter, can see them as they fly over. The professional wildfowlers of The Wash - men like Kenzie Thorpe and Frank Harrison - used pieces of newspaper with clods of mud to weigh them down, to represent the tails of feeding pinkfeet. The important thing is to get the pattern right. If everything appears as natural as possible the fowl have the confidence to drop in and attempt to join the decoys.

"Hare come Harry!" exclaimed Frank, and we looked up to see a largish motorboat ploughing across the now fully flooded harbour towards our point.

"Make sure your boots are clean else you'll har to walk hoome." added Frank with a grin. The boat glided in until the stem just touched the shore and the tide pushed in the stern, making it simple to hop on board. Swinging over the tiller, Harry steered us out into deeper water before opening up the throttle. It took I suppose, half an hour to chug across the wide sheltered waters, waters that glittered now in the morning sunlight. We leant against the gunwales of the boat, wind in our faces, dog's tails thumping against our legs, as we surveyed the picturesque scene. Our guns lay silent as the cries of wildfowl were carried with us to the shore.

25

December 23

Christmas was upon us once again, catching most of us unawares as usual, but the chances of a white Christmas looked distinctly remote. I had driven over to Norfolk the previous evening and when we retired to bed there was a slight frost beneath a sky glittering with a million stars. The last thoughts I could remember before sleep overcame me, were pleasurable ones of the beautifully crisp morning that we could reasonably expect. I awoke before daybreak to the sound of water running off the roof! Evidently cloud had materialized and the temperature had risen considerably during the night. With these conditions there would almost certainly be more rain. Fortunately this initial precipitation cleared up with the coming of daylight and I suspect that my spirits were not the only ones that rose slightly with the barometer. We had a morning's pheasant shooting lined up on the farm of George's neighbour Andrew, and a dry day is always preferable to the alternative. During the drive to the farm, Alec explained that Andrew's acreage was not large enough to extend to a full day's shooting. He relied on wild birds, but there were usually enough of them wandering around the farm to ensure a very enjoyable morning. There are normally five or six guns including one or two that like to work their dogs. The latter always volunteer to act as beaters or walking guns. Whenever possible it is a regular team, which not surprisingly provokes a certain amount of banter and provides opportunities for eye-wipes.

Two cars were already in the yard when we turned in, but they had only just arrived, as the occupants were either busy rummaging in the vehicles for cartridges or pulling on boots. I recognised George and his nephew Tom, but I did not know the other two men. We parked the car and walked towards them when a tall man with a bald patch, joined the group.

"That's Andrew, our host," said Alec indicating the newcomer. Andrew strode over to shake Alec warmly by the hand and with a twinkle asked if he had any shot in his cartridges today.

"I ruddy well hope so," laughed my friend, introducing me first to Andrew and then to Roger and Don, the other two guns. The party were laughing at Don's expense because he, being a chain smoker, had lit up a cigarette before his feet had left the car. He then proceeded to have a good cough, after which he declared himself fighting fit for the next few hours.

The terrain was all new to me so I resolved to fall in with anything that was asked of me. It was gently undulating country with one main wood and a couple of spinneys. Andrew marshalled the troops ready to work in the outlying fields and so encourage any game to make for the wood. Roger and Don, with their labradors and an English springer spaniel, were detailed to walk via the main road until they could enter the farm again unseen at the boundary hedge. The rest of us were to take a hedge each and work them

161

slowly towards the boundary, but to ensure we waited for Roger and Don. I came to a gate in my particular hedge and peered through the gap. A little way along the hedge bottom, a cock pheasant was walking away from me. I judged him to be a hundred yards distant and knew if I flushed him carelessly, he would fly straight for the boundary. I deliberately made a movement, which he spotted at once. I remained hidden behind the hedge, but he knew from whence the movement came and ran out into the field away from the suspected danger. Once he was running in the right direction I showed myself. As I anticipated, he took wing, sailing straight to the wood.

At the boundary hedge I waited for the others to work down towards me. They were still a considerable way off when they flushed a good covey of partridges. wings set, the covey skimmed over the hedge and away over a stubble, just too wide for a shot. The dogs came hunting along the hedge well ahead of their respective masters, but they did not flush anything for me. The others had collected a brace of pheasants that had chosen to head the wrong way. We worked the fields and the long boundary hedge, putting up four more birds that flew safely towards the wood.

We split up while we were still far enough from the wood to avoid any possible disturbance. The standing guns would be Alec, me, George and young Tom. The four of us needed to make a long detour to take us round to the far end of the wood. Don, Roger and Andrew, who had elected to join them, allowed us ten or fifteen minutes to get into position before commencing their thrash through the undergrowth. The wood was quite small, perhaps covering no more than three or four acres and was longer than it was wide. The three 'beaters' taking equal portions, could easily cover it in one drive through. I noticed some feed hoppers and bins in places convenient for topping up.

When we reached the chosen spot, George and Alec set about deciding where we should stand. Eventually we spread out at intervals of about forty-five yards, waiting for whatever might come forward during the next ten minutes or so. Finding myself standing on rough grass, I stamped a level patch for a firm footing. Loading the gun I looked round first to see where the other guns were standing and then to take in the surroundings. The land sloped away to the right and rose again to another ridge six hundred yards away. Directly behind was a large wood beyond the boundary, and it was to here that any game coming out of our wood would head. Far behind on the right flank was another small wood, where a stalker's high seat was visible in one corner.

A blackbird flitted through the trees uttering his alarm call, and at once my ears picked up the sound of sticks tapping and dogs being scolded. A few moments later I heard a clatter of wings. Within seconds, a corking cock pheasant came belting out of the treetops. He went straight over Alec, up to a point before folding to the first shot of the drive. The walking guns were getting shots at birds breaking back, but enough came forward to keep everyone on their toes. There followed a hectic few minutes of clatter and crowing from the wood, whirring wings and hurtling shapes of brown, red and gold. Some fell in a puff of feathers, but others flew on to the peace and security of the big wood. The 'ping' of ejectors throwing out the empty cases and the sting and stink of powder smoke, all contributed to these thrilling moments. Before long though, the dogs appeared at the end of the wood and it was time to break the gun. Eleven pheasants and a rabbit were claimed as the fruits of that little drive.

From the wood we walked up a lengthy hill and it was not long before even the fittest of the group was breathing a little more heavily.

"This'll give your heart some good exercise George!" Don panted.

George, who in recent years had undergone triple by-pass surgery, could only agree.

"Well," put in Alec. "if he keels over, nobody here will give him mouth-to-mouth resuscitation."

"No," laughed Don, "You never know, he might be faking it!" And so we bantered our way up the long hill and beyond, until we had reached the far end of a forty-acre meadow. Lining out again, with the dog men taking in the hedges, we walked the whole meadow down to a small spinney, which was beaten through. The occasional shot presented itself and a bird or two found their way into the bag. There were several hares on the meadow and one was shot as it made for the hedge.

The morning progressed until we had walked back past the main wood. Beyond a little valley, stood another small wood on higher ground. We lined the valley while Don and Roger entered this wood from the rear. Pheasants flushed now, would most probably head across to the main wood and offer opportunities for shots at pretty high birds. Of course not everything goes to plan when you are dealing with wild birds. Of the half-dozen that were flushed, three flew wide, one was missed and two remained with us. The first bird to leave the wood was in fact, a very disgruntled tawny owl. Being on the night shift, this chap did not seem best pleased by this unexpected and noisy disruption of his daytime slumbers.

Down the gradual incline we trooped, the leading guns alert for any bird skulking in the hedge bottoms, until we found ourselves passing a stack of hay at the entrance to the yard. The rain returned as we took it in turns to wash the mud off our boots in a running ditch that was nearby, but it was not going to inconvenience us now. Our boot cleaning completed we laid out the bag, braced them up and hung them from the rafters of Andrew's workshop. Twelve brace, a couple of rabbits and the hare - not a big day by some folk's standards, but a pleasant sporting morning enjoyed with pleasant sporting people.

Andrew beckoned us all into the farmhouse kitchen, where his wife June was waiting with coffee and a fair mountain of sausage rolls and mince pies, piping hot from the aga. While the triumphs and disasters of the morning were cheerfully discussed and analysed, the food miraculously vanished as quickly as ice sluiced with boiling water. After such a spread it was difficult to get up and leave, but at last everyone exchanged the season's greetings and went their separate ways, no doubt to make final preparations for the few days of festivity.

26

January 5

Another morning flight on the north Norfolk shore was on the cards and this simple fact ensured my journey into that fair county on the Friday was full of anticipation. When I arrived at the cottage just after noon, Alec was waiting in the yard and could hardly wait until the car had drawn to a standstill before he was at the side window.

"I've had a word with Frank and he suggests that we go for the evening flight tonight and then stay over in the pub so that we're on the spot for the morning. What do you think?"

"That's fine by me," I replied. "There will still be the last of the moon. Do you think that it will mess up the morning?

"Well, it didn't last time," said Alec. "Frank says that as it's a tide flight, things should be all right. The duck will still want to spend the day in the sheltered waters of the harbour."

With the plan agreed, I did not bother to off-load my baggage from the car. Instead we went indoors for a cup of tea with Molly while Alec sorted out his own paraphernalia in readiness for the coming foray. Within three quarters of an hour we were unloading the car, but this time at a welcoming pub in the little coastal village. As Frank had informed the landlord that we would be going out early in the morning, we had been billeted in an annex to the main building, or rather what appeared to have been an adjoining cottage at one time. The door opened onto a narrow street, which led down the quay and all its associated boats. The quarters could not have suited our purpose better. At three o'clock we sought out Frank, who had arranged to meet us down on the hard. We saw his pick-up first, and then spotted his burly figure chatting to someone attending to a boat. He caught sight of us at the same time and raised his hand in acknowledgement.

A moment or two later our friendly guide came over for a few words before releasing an excited spaniel and collecting his gun from the pick-up. We followed Frank as he waded across the sandy-bottomed channel and headed along the course of an old pilot path that meandered across the salt-marsh. He stationed us well apart, along the brink of a winding creek. Some curlew and brent geese put on quite a show for us as dusk crept stealthily over the marsh. Several teal buzzed about chirruping to each other, but studiously ignored my attempts to call them.

When it was too dark to see distant birds, three shots rang out in a ragged burst. They must have turned a single teal in my direction because there, seen for a fraction of a second, black against an orange patch of sky, scorched a tiny speeding blob. Somehow my snap-shot connected and the blob dropped to the mud. I was about to climb out of the creek to begin a search, but then thought better of it, deciding that it would be best to stay put. After all, I had marked the bird down and knew exactly where it was. Moreover, the others would be returning this way with the dog before long. In fact in a matter of ten minutes, I could hear the splashing footsteps and the muffled murmur of

167

voices as the others approached. I stood up as they appeared from the shadows, and within seconds the little spaniel had brought in my teal. Frank had another in his bag. That evening in the pub Frank joined us for a pint or two of best bitter and told us where to meet him in the morning. As we left for our quarters his last cheery words were.

"I've laid on transport so don't be late!"

There was no chance whatsoever of being late for our rendezvous. We were awake well before it was time to leave and even had time for a shave and a cup of black sweet tea. We drove a couple of miles to a point where an embanked road wound its way across the marshes until it ended abruptly at the base of the huge shingle bank. The North Sea could be heard in the darkness beyond the bank, groaning continuously as its waves pounded the beach with incessant ferocity.

We sat in the car considering what possible transport could have been laid on for such tricky terrain as this. We were not to be left in suspense for long. Lights appeared, making a wavering progress along the marsh road and then we could hear the unmistakable sound of a tractor. Sure enough, in due course a Fordson Major rumbled noisily to a halt and its driver dismounted.

"Har ye waiting for Frank?" he asked cheerily. On our replying in the affirmative, he went on. "I'm his brother Ted. I'm going bait digging and Frank asked me to give you a lift. He'll be hare in jiffy I shouldn't wonder. I'll bet he'll have an excuse - allus bloody does!"

As if in reply, Frank's headlights appeared at that very moment. No sooner had he stepped out of the truck than he set about confirming his brother's prophecy.

"Cor dear, old Chris came into the pub last night, after you'd gone. I couldn't get away, we didn't get hoome 'til one this morning."

Fixed to the lifting arms on the rear of the tractor, was what can only be described as a large stout wooden box, about five feet by three feet and three feet in depth. It was secured across the width of the tractor so that the three feet protruded behind. The box contained the bait digging fork and buckets, plus a pair of labrador retrievers, who became very interested when they noticed our guns. Somehow the three of us, along with Frank's spaniel, squeezed into the box. There we stood in a row, hanging onto a crossbar of angle iron that ran across in front of us. That crossbar was to prove vital.

"Hold tight!" shouted Ted as he raised up the lifting arms a couple of feet and let in the clutch. The tractor lurched forward, climbed the shingle bank and set off along the top underneath the night sky. As one would expect, the shingle was very loose and it was near impossible to steer a straight course. In fact, Ted kept his wheels in the same rutted tracks that he used on most journeys along this bank. It was almost like a railway train, bound to follow wherever the rails should lead. In this case, it was a very erratic course indeed and we all hung on for grim death as we swung from side to side. What made it more exciting was the fact that Ted chose to drive without lights, as he did not want to advertise his activities to all and sundry. It was not as difficult as it might sound, for the sky was lightening with the breaking dawn and to our right the sea reflected the light.

The three of us lurched into each other with every swing and sway, the dogs leaning hard against the backs of our legs as they hung on in their own way. I could imagine claws digging into the wooden floor. We bantered away above the roar of the engine, as occasional sparks spewed from the exhaust showing momentarily as orange specks before our eyes. We rushed along like charioteers from hell. It was certainly a ride I would not forget in a hurry and I wouldn't have missed it for the world. As Ted brought us to a crunching halt in the lee of a sand dune I began to laugh.

"That must be as near to sidecar racing as you can get!"

Frank and Alec couldn't agree more.

Ted came with us as we walked out over the salt-marsh and it suddenly occurred to me that our party had returned to the same channel we had ambushed during our previous visit a month ago. Then we had approached using Shank's pony, not a bait diggers tractor, so I forgave myself my initial lack of observation!

The brothers tossed out weighted decoys along the channel, before Ted left us to get on with his bait digging. He had shot near this spot fairly recently and had taken two wigeon and two pintail. Alec and I were in opposite hiding places to last time, while Frank posted himself beyond Alec, nearer the estuary.

Light came apace now, with gulls and curlew soon on the move. I could hear wigeon too and then spotted a small company of them heading up the harbour. A shape loomed up to my left, following the channel - a curlew. It was gratifying to note that he didn't spot me until level with my gutter. Once the bird saw me he made enough fuss about it and veered off sharply. It was a wasted effort, for I held my fire hoping for duck.

"Look up Alec!" came a shout from Frank.

I turned to seek the cause of the warning. I didn't know what Alec was supposed to be looking for, but I found a duck speeding along the channel about twenty feet above the mud. It was well past by the time I fired, but it folded and dropped neatly near a bend in the waterway. Thinking it might have fallen into the already flooding channel, with the dog two hundred yards away; I waded across the channel and along the far side to where the bird fell. It was not drifting away round the bend so I assumed it was laying hidden amongst the samphire. I knew it was dead and therefore safe to leave for the spaniel so I hurried back to my hiding place. Two shots rang out from the others, but I could not see what they were shooting at. It transpired that they had both missed a pack of wigeon.

I was surprised to see Frank suddenly gathering in the decoys. He came up to join me and told me that the tide had come in three quarters of an hour early, so we would soon have to move back. He waded across the channel to search for my fallen duck and as he was climbing out onto the marsh, four wigeon came along high overhead. My second shot brought one down no more than a hundred yards from Frank, who hurried across the mud with the dog. Incredibly, the bird must have ran to a nearby creek and dived, for it was never seen again. It happens occasionally and I hate it when it does. Luck was with us regarding the other bird though, for as Frank re-crossed the channel and worked his way back to me, I was able to tell him exactly when he was opposite the fall. The spaniel swam over and found it in a trice. It was an immature cock wigeon, just getting the colour to his head, but not yet possessing the vivid white shoulders of his elders.

The tide was coming up into the smaller creeks and gutters now and we were forced to retreat back to the sand-hills and the tractor, which was standing there mute, awaiting it's master. Ted was making his way back with a bucket of lugworms. He was destined to be one of the few remaining diggers on this coast. A coast, which once boasted gangs who dug enough worms to provide bait for sea anglers nationwide. When he got back we all piled in to our 'chariot' for the return journey along the shingle bank, this time in daylight. A wild sea crashed white foam to our left and the now flooded marshes with the harbour beyond, delighting our eyes to the right. We observed several duck sitting safe and secure on some of the wider creeks. I asked why, in the absence of wind, the tide had come in so early. Frank pointed out a swell on the sea, indicating he said, strong winds to come, winds had already affected the tides.

We were invited back to Frank's house in a neighbouring village where he kindly fried us a breakfast of bacon and eggs accompanied by slabs of thick buttered toast and scalding hot black coffee. Then, aware that he was going to sea later that morning, we thanked our generous host for his hospitality and set off back to Alec's home.

27

January 12

In the middle of the week, the ring of the telephone reached my ears just as my wife and I were getting into the car on our way out for a drink with some friends. I hesitated, tempted to ignore the call, but in the end decided to answer the wretched thing. How glad I was that I chose to do so. It was Alec, asking if I could possibly go over to his cottage on the Thursday evening, as he had some goose shooting lined up for Friday morning. It so happened that I was free on Friday so I accepted without hesitation.

As we faced each other across the hearth on that Thursday evening, watching the orange sparks flicker up the blackened chimneybreast, Alec outlined the situation. The geese that from time to time visited Uncle Edgar's water meadows, had recently decided to move over onto his neighbour's winter wheat. The gentleman in question was none too pleased at the prospect of a hundred odd pairs of great webbed feet paddling all over his crop, to say nothing of what they were pulling up to eat. As a rule, farmers do not object too much if pinkfeet begin grazing on the wheat, provided the weather is

173

frosty. In times of frost, the plant is cropped rather than uprooted and this can even be beneficial to the resulting crop. In days gone by, some farmers have been known to turn sheep out on winter wheat to eat off the top in the same way. Moreover, pinkfeet usually move on after a day or so. In this instance the geese were the greylags that were more or less, resident birds at a local lake. They could easily return again and again to the same fields. The other problem was that a lack of frost meant that the corn was being uprooted. Drastic measures were called for and fortunately for us, Uncle Edgar had sought assistance from Alec. There was a slight hitch, in that Rosy had injured her leg during the day. Alec didn't want to risk exacerbating the problem, so we reluctantly decided to leave her at home on the morrow.

The next morning was dark, with just a hint of mist swirling about in the beams of the headlights during the short journey to the water meadows. We parked the car on Edgar's land and after pulling on boots and coats, strode eagerly to the neighbour's wheat field. The field was immediately behind the meadows, where the land began to rise with a gentle slope. There was a ditch between the two fields, with one or two blackthorn bushes dotted along its length. I remembered that in September, Alec and his wife Molly had gathered enough sloes from these same bushes for this year's batch of sloe gin. Along the headland, running parallel to the ditch was a strip of low cover for the benefit of game. There were patches of slightly taller vegetation, standing three feet tall and so a perfect place to hide in ambush.

Approximately half-a-mile in front of our cover, the river meandered through meadows, until it passed through the mill on the outskirts of a village that lay hidden in the dank darkness of this winter's morning. At dawn, twenty wigeon came into view, flying from the direction of the river. They flew true like a sheaf of arrows, right over my head, no more than sixty feet above the ground. I swung the barrels of the magnum through them, but reluctantly held my fire. The shooting was let on this land and we were allowed geese only, although that was far from a cause for complaint. It is funny though isn't it? Whenever there is some reason that prevents you from taking a shot, a good opportunity is certain to present itself.

Half an hour after the wigeon had made their flight, a shot from Alec shattered the silence and sent rooks complaining noisily from their roosts. It made me jump too, as I had been unaware of anything approaching. Alec had fired his shot at a skein of geese that had slipped in quietly. I heard them depart, but I never did see them.

"Missed," came the muttered response to the unasked question.

Not so long afterwards I spotted a sizeable silhouette in flight and judged that it must pass within range of my friend's hiding place. Sure enough, moments later, a sharp stab of orange flame pierced the darkness. This was followed by the report, which coincided with the fall of the great bird. Hearing the almighty thump when it hit the ground, Alec remained in position in case more geese were on the move. None were seen or heard for quite some time, so Alec went out to collect his bird. It soon became apparent that he could not find the goose, so I went to help. We scoured the cover all around with no success and had to conclude that despite that hefty fall it wasn't dead and had walked off under cover of darkness.

"Damnation!" Alec cursed. "I ought to have picked it straight away. It was a canada and I felt certain it was dead." We resolved that as we had been unable to bring Rosy, we must pick up any further birds at once, unless we could see them.

It was light when a party of greylags arrived. This bunch came in from the river and I made rather a mess of the chance taking two shots at the same goose. I knew I had shaken it and so kept an eye on it. Suddenly the stricken bird left the skein and fell well out in the field. The bird was in full view, but after our earlier experience I walked out to collect it straight away. Before I reached it, however, I could see that it was stone dead.

A clamour of goose music heralded the arrival of two or three lines of greys and canadas, which seemed to come together and merge into mixed parties. They were not bothering to sneak in quietly now. A jumble of wavering lines came in nicely and I took out a right and left, one of each species. I kept down and reloaded as fast as I could. The grey mass of geese was milling round in confusion having come under fire from Alec. One party broke away and careered back over my head, enabling to me take another easy right and left. Mind you, they are only easy when they come off!

We had brought with us some short lengths of bamboo cane, normally reserved for tomatoes in the garden, and we used these to set up our geese as decoys. By simply inserting one end into the bill and the other into the ground, the geese appeared to be sitting on the wheat. The only drawback was that, using this method, they all had their heads straight up, as though alert and ready to fly. However, it didn't seem to worry the skeins that came in later. The canadas came in twice. They were wide of me, but Alec had his chances and made the most of them. I was watching him retrieve one bird that had fallen near a ditch, when another goose suddenly scrambled up and ran across the field. It was the 'lost' bird.

Luckily, Alec had taken his gun with him and was able to despatch it before it had travelled far. It was a relief to both of us that the runner had been accounted for.

The main crowd of geese had either gone back to the lake or were trying a fresh field, for only small skeins or single birds now visited us. When we packed up, we found that we had killed ten geese, which, with the exception of my two greylags, were all canadas. We had to make two return journeys to the car, laden with geese and equipment.

Back in the farmyard Edgar was delighted with our success, both for his neighbour's sake and the fact that he had promised several friends a goose. It was nice to know that he had such confidence in our ability! We were more than happy for him to have the birds, although we did retain the two greylags for ourselves. Now he was almost begging us to come again the next morning. Alec was uncertain.

"I don't know Edgar." He said. "We've given them quite a roasting this morning, you know. I can't imagine that they will want to push their luck again so soon."

"Well, George and young Tom would like to come tomorrow," Edgar persisted. "And I'd like you to come as well. If the geese don't come back that's all well and good, but if they do, it will really give them the message. Anyway, I've still got people who want a bird. Will you come?"

Alec grinned.

"All right, for you old fellow - but don't blame me if we all wait around for nothing."

When, at 6.30 the next morning, Alec and I arrived at the field gate to the water meadows, we found George and his nephew already there and raring to go. We set off at once for the wheat field and as we walked I offered to go to the far end of the field, and leave my place for one of the others. However, Alec suggested that we take up the same positions

177

as yesterday and let George and Tom cover the end of the field, as several geese had come and gone over there and had not been shot at. They might just feel that it was safe to feed there. Unfortunately, George and Tom had to leave at 8.00 o'clock so we hoped that if birds were going to come, they would come early.

In the dark waiting in my cover, I pondered on the chances of geese attempting to feed on this wheat so soon after being ambushed, and decided that we would be unlucky if the odd one or two didn't come to see how the breakfast table looked. We had been waiting for close on an hour before it was light enough to see very far. Duck had certainly been on the move in the vicinity of the river for some time. What was that? I could have sworn... then - "Aank! Annkle! Annkleannkle!" No mistaking that - the sound of greylag on the move. Eyes straining under the peak of my cap, trying to penetrate the gloom, then I made them out, four large shapes heading straight for me and low. I allowed them to come right in and as I rose to shoot, they flared away to the right. Boom! Boom! The reports echoed around the hedgerows, and two geese flung back their necks and fell thump, thud into the cover. The survivors followed the line of the ditch. I saw Alec's gun suddenly appear and was surprised when he missed. The geese were climbing by the time they got to George who pulled one down in fine style.

While all this was happening, a skein of fifteen had come in from the other direction over Tom. I heard his shots and looked up to see that his skein was hurrying away from him, but the birds would come past me as they made tracks for the lake. The skein was high - forty yards, just time for one shot and for a moment I thought I'd muffed it as the tail of the selected goose dropped, but then it somersaulted backwards,

178

over and over, whirling down stone dead. I gathered my birds and quickly set them out as decoys.

For the next half an hour geese turned up in ones and twos, probably scouting the field to see if we had cleared off. Luckily, George and Tom got some chances before they left. Soon after they had gone, four lots of around fifty canadas flew along the river completely ignoring our field and I was pretty sure that we would see no more of them.

In fact, one more big lot did turn up. We had not had a shot for some time and I suppose the quietness gave them confidence, or it was possible that they had seen George and Tom leaving. Anyway, come they did and Alec took a tidy right and left from the end of the line. As the canadas noisily made their exit over a distant hedge, we decided that enough was enough. Today's bag was nine geese, but of course the other two guns had taken their birds so the load was not quite as heavy. A few days later Alec received a grateful telephone call from Uncle Edgar to say that the wheat field had been devoid of geese ever since. Given the circumstances it was hardly surprising.

28

January 17

A dusting of snow followed by a quick thaw and heavy rainfall brought up the water levels on the washes almost overnight. The run off from higher land in neighbouring counties put added pressure onto the already swollen rivers. Within three days the floods were well and truly out on the washes, which of course was the very purpose for which they had been created. I telephoned Alec at once; we had been waiting for some water all season. This we reckoned was better late than never, but we needed to take advantage as soon as possible. To this end Alec agreed to come over in time for a try at dusk on the Wednesday and a crack-of-dawn show on the Thursday. When my friend duly arrived on Wednesday, I was ready and waiting so we lost no time in heading off at once.

We motored to a spot a mile to the east of our last visit, along a pothole-ridden gravelled drove that was completely underwater in parts. As the potholes were therefore hidden from view it made for an interesting drive. Second gear was definitely the order of the day. Ever the optimist, Alec commented that at least it was giving the wheel arches a good wash. That was true and I reminded myself to try the brakes when we left this watery domain. The gravel petered out and the drove continued as a black muddy morass. I was determined to go no further and turned the car one hundred and eighty degrees and parked on firm dry ground. Would it still be firm when we returned after dark? I wondered. Would the water have risen? I reflected that we were a good mile from the main road, and not for the first time wished my car was a Land Rover. Then a pack of wigeon came whistling overhead driving all such negative thoughts out of our heads, causing us to gather up our guns and bags to hurry away along the drove as fast as the clinging mud would allow.

Where to hide? That was the question. There seemed to be no set pattern. Duck were everywhere and anywhere, criss-crossing the sky in bunches, packs, arcs, teams and companies all going nowhere in particular, or so it seemed to us. We decided that wigeon would be the most likely of the different species to stay on the washes. They would feed on the short grasses at dusk. Searching for fields with enough grass showing above the water presented us with our next problem, but at last we found one and set about finding cover. I selected a thick fencepost surrounded by stalks of long dead nettles, while Alec chose to stay back behind the more obvious cover of the gate with its stout post and rails.

A fresh wind blew from the southwest as dusk approached and while lapwings seemed to battle against it, it had no such effect on the duck, which coursed up and down at an average height of a hundred yards. The darkness closed in and as the sight of wildfowl lessened so the sounds of them became the more evident. Whistles, growls, croaks and quacks, the prrripp of the pintail and louder than most, the whoop of the

Bewick's swans. A long line of the latter beat noisily to their chosen roost and I watched them go. As they disappeared into the darkness, three mallard appeared from the opposite direction. I gripped the magnum but purely as a reaction, as they were going to pass some way off. My eyes followed the flickering shapes until they were well out of sight. As usual, it was quite dark before the wigeon deigned to move and for a few minutes the sky was full of the rushing wings and wild calls that thrill us to the very core. Pack after pack after pack passed unseen on either side and right over our heads. Wherever they had chosen as their feeding quarters for the night, it certainly was not our field. We splashed and slid our way back to the car with clean barrels. Jet led the way; pleased to be relieved of his dutiful wait at my side and now busy investigating every gateway he passed.

Alec had noticed the riverside public house on the edge of these washes and commented on its unusual name. It is indeed unusual, and if there is another 'Dog-in-a-Doublet' in the United Kingdom I have yet to hear of its whereabouts. As he was interested I suggested we should go and sample the pub's best bitter. While we sat enjoying our pints, I told him that the inn is mentioned at length in the pages of *Sporting Sketches at Home and Abroad,* a long out-of-print volume by one Horace William Wheelwright, son of the then Rector of Tansor near Oundle, Northamptonshire.

Wheelwright contributed articles to *The Field* magazine in the nineteenth century under the *nom-de-plume* 'Old Bushman'. In his book he describes an overnight stay at the Dog-in-a-Doublet around 1845, prior to a snipe shooting expedition into the surrounding fens. I asked the landlord if he had a copy of the book.

"No, but I did have some copies made of the passage you are referring to - they're part of the local appeal, though you're the first in years to enquire. Pointing to a bookshelf at the back of the room, he went on.

"They're gathering dust over there - help yourself."

I collected a pamphlet, found the account, and quietly read parts of it to Alec.

'The heavy mist was rising fast, obscuring the few landmarks visible by daylight in this dreary waste; and it was with no little satisfaction that I hailed a glimmering light shining murkily through the window of the solitary public house halfway down the bank, which was to be my headquarters for the night...

'I made my way into the kitchen of the inn (the bar-parlour of this sporting snuggery), attracted by the blazing light in the open hearth, contrasting well with the gloomy landscape I was leaving outside. A glance around the room at once discovered the owner's calling and another at the chimney corner showed me the owner himself. Two or three lumbering, huge punt-guns, all upon the flint and steel principle, hung from the rafters; a crazy hand gun for stopping the cripples stood in one corner; while sprits stalking poles and setting sticks, nets of every variety and huge water-boots were stowed away wherever space could be found for them.

'The king of the fen gunners now stood before me, nearly seventy years of age, short, but compactly built, his old weather-beaten face something resembling the turf sods that lay in his hearth. The few scanty locks combed over his wrinkled forehead plainly told that he had reached the period of years usually allotted to man; yet the active motion, the spare, erect figure and above all the bright grey eye, also as plainly told that the hand of time had dealt lightly with him. Bred in the fen, his whole life had been spent in its solitudes, and his whole little world centred in this rude spot. Rarely indeed did he visit the haunts of his fellow men, except when the autumn floods drove the birds into the uplands and he made certain periodical trips up the river with his punt and big gun. Scarcely cognisant of what was going on in the outer world, he was nevertheless perfectly at home in his own peculiar district; and, rich in lowland lore, a rare fund of reliable information regarding the fauna of the fen, the results of more than half a century's experience, flowed glibly from the lips of one who had probably never opened a book in his life.

'After that night of sound repose, which no one enjoys better than the sportsman, I was up betimes. The weather had cleared, the wind blew gently from the west and it was a day of all others for snipe shooting. To describe the days sport would be superfluous, one day's snipe shooting so much resembles another. The splashing through the reed beds and marshy meadows; the jumps of the fen ditches; the scape of the rising snipe; the "Well killed, master," of the guide when a good shot was made - are familiar to every sportsman. Suffice it to say that I never had a better day on the fen than my last.

'Nine and a half couples of snipe, three mallard, five teal, was the bag; and the last shot I fired in the fen I can remember as if it were but yesterday, for we had nearly reached home and as I was climbing over a gate, two mallard rose from a fen dyke close to me and I made a good wind-up by killing them right and left.

'That the old place should ever be drained and a railway carried into the heart of the fen was past my belief. The old duck-man has long since been gathered to his fathers and it is possible even that the old 'Cross Guns' or 'Dog-in-a-Doublet' has been whitewashed up and shines forth in cockneyfied array as the 'Railway Hotel'.'

When I had finished reading the passage, I told Alec that Wheelwright died at as a young man and could not have known that although the railway was indeed carried through the heart of the fen, and there is a 'Railway Hotel', both the railway and the hotel are at least two miles north of the 'Dog-in a-Doublet'. Thankfully, the old inn retained its name and stands to this day on the banks of the river overlooking the washlands. Those cattle marshes are still home to the same species of fowl, fish and wildfowlers not so very different from the old landlord who shot here all those years ago. By the time I had passed on that little history lesson to my friend our pint pots were as drained as most of the old fen.

Early the next morning, we were once more squelching in the darkness along that long drove that cut straight as an arrow through the washlands, making for the same positions that we had occupied at dusk only a few hours previously. I gathered some hay from a broken bale that had fallen from the load in the summer and made a dry seat for Jet, adding some more to my meagre cover. This done I settled to await the dawn and whatever it might bring. The eastern sky gradually transformed to a pattern of blue-grey over a backdrop of pale grey, in whorls similar to those found inside the glass marbles we played with at school. They stretched in broad-brush strokes across the sky, as if daubed on the canvas by a surrealist artist who, in a frenzy of sudden inspiration, must record his vision before it passed. And of course, it did pass. Within minutes the rising sun, although not yet above the horizon, lit the undersides of the grey clouds with a tinge of salmon pink, which spread and spread again, until the whole prospect to the east was a glorious panorama of pink and grey.

I knelt, totally and utterly absorbed by the scene even though I had seen hundreds like it. No two sunrises are exactly the same and almost all, provide that uplifting feeling of thankfulness that one should be alive and privileged to be part of such a beautiful scene. Not all of us can find employment that allows the freedom to live thus, but if you can, it is well worth taking half the salary gained by commuting to an office job in the rush and tear of the city. Whether they realise it or not, living closer to nature free of stress and with space to move and breathe is the preferred natural state for most people, and is a prime ingredient for a life of contentment.

These thoughts passed through my mind and concentration momentarily lapsed. I was brought to earth by a shrill whistle from Alec and looked towards him to see what was afoot. He gesticulated wildly until I spotted the cause of all the excitement; a small skein of pinkfeet was approaching from behind me. They had come in quietly and even now were not calling. I dare not move and so crouched as low as I could among the dead nettle stalks, hissing at the dog to stay still. He turned his big brown eyes upon me with a quizzical look and thumped his tail on the grass; apart from that, thankfully he remained quiet. The geese crossed the dyke over a hundred yards from me, but only forty-five yards up. If only I had hidden a bit further along, what a chance it would have been.

There was no time to contemplate what might have been because even before the geese were out of sight, a crescendo of whistling told of wigeon on the move, and a good crowd of them by the sound of it. They followed a similar line to the geese, but there were many more of them and they came in a great wave that stretched over a wide area. It became clear that we should both be in with a chance. I usually perform better with a snapshot than at birds I can see coming from a long way off, but today the gods were with me. As the wave of duck hurtled above with a rush of rapidly flickering wings, both barrels connected and I had achieved a right and left. A second wave followed close behind, not at all put off by our shots at their predecessors. They were just too wide for me, but squarely over Alec. I watched in fascination as two wigeon tumbled from the pack to hit the water behind him in twin spurts of spray. Jet made his own spray as he bounded out to the fall. It transpired that while I was occupied with my own birds, Alec had also taken one from the first wave.

Looking back at the sky I noticed that all signs of pink had vanished. In an effort to break through the curtain of cloud, the sun now showed as a brilliant patch behind a screen of dull grey. An hour later the atmosphere became hazy and then misty as the sun's warmth drew up moisture. By now we were trudging happily back to the car and before we reached it, the solar star had prevailed to conquer the clouds and bathe us in sunlight. Trips of fowl were, as yesterday, constantly on the move, but heavens high. The bulk of them were wigeon and teal of course, with occasional teams of mallard and pintail. A little party of shoveler sped by. These were lower and the light conditions showed vividly the demarcation between the chestnut belly and the rest of the plumage. Because of this, the obviously dark heads of the drakes seemed to fly separately, ahead of the bodies.

We were not tempted to stay on - it had been a successful flight and we had more than enough in our bags for our immediate needs.

29

January 20

The weekend again! Alec had brought Tom over late on the Friday evening, with the intention of ambushing the wigeon on their flight along the flooded washlands next morning. We were forced into a change of plan by the weather. The clear skies attending the new moon had brought some severe frosts and the temperature had not been much above freezing point at midday. As a result the shallow floodwaters had quickly iced over, pushing a lot of the duck onto the nearby tidal river. The three of us were bubbling with anticipation in the early morning darkness, as we drove to my friend Chris's farm that lies adjacent to the riverbank. The puddles were frozen on the long bumpy road that ran down past the house and yard. Some of them crunched as the ice shattered under the weight of the wheels, but most did not. I think they were frozen solid.

We left the car near the dilapidated barn, which disgorged feral pigeons with a clatter like bats emerging from the dark recesses of a sinister cavern. Even before it began to get light we could see that the world was white, with every reed, every fence post, every strand of wire and every blade of grass with its own individual coating of hoar frost. It dusted our boots as we plodded along under the bank and Jet gambolled about in delight, insulated by his thick fur coat, seemingly immune to the cold. This time Tom and I shared the hide near the fence, while Alec moved downstream and tucked himself into a little rush filled nook in the brink.

For all the anticipation, the movement of wildfowl at dawn was disappointing to say the least. In fact it was almost non-existent. A long line of Bewick's swans became noisily airborne and whooped their way westwards, no doubt to spend the day on someone's winter wheat. A spring of teal came tearing along the centre of the river about four feet above the surface. They towered when we moved and sped onwards unaffected by four rapid shots.

When it was fully light, I went higher up the bank so that I could see over onto the washlands. There, beyond the far riverbank, was a large sheet of floodwater a good thirty acres in area and completely frozen over. Nevertheless the duck were there, or at least the wigeon were. Tight bunches, smaller parties and bigger companies were dotted all over the ice showing as black dots against the grey-white backdrop. As I watched through my field-glasses, a marsh harrier glided low over one group causing them to take flight. I cannot think that the harrier posed much of a threat to a healthy wigeon, but they certainly did not like the raptor being too close for comfort. The flushed birds did not fly far, they merely joined a larger pack on the far side of the ice. I moved back down to the hide, not feeling very optimistic. I poured a cup of coffee for Tom and myself from the thermos flask and as we sipped the warming fluid, I told him what I had seen.

An hour passed with nothing more than the odd pigeon coming anywhere near, until I saw a knotted bunch of dots buzzing along the river towards Alec's position. I nudged Tom.

"Look up, Alec's going to get a shot here."

However, the dots momentarily doubled in size as they braked and pitched on the river, some way before they reached my friend. We could see his head peering round his cover and as the duck swam into our side of the river, Alec crept out over the slamp and bending double began to stalk the fowl.

"He won't get anywhere near them," I said confidently to Tom, but then I saw the strategy. Half-a-dozen sheep were grazing between Alec and the duck and provided he did not scare them, he might be able to use them as a sort of stalking horse. Duck are used to seeing livestock grazing and take no notice of them even if they are quite close. In the past I have gently moved cattle along in order to walk up among them, but sheep are skittish at the best of times so I did not hold out much hope for Alec's plan.

In the event, it half-worked. Before he was properly within range the sheep decided he was too close to them and scurried off. At once the ducks became totally alert - all heads were raised. The saving grace was that they were divers. I could see that now as they ran along the surface to take off, and the wind was such that they had to fly towards Alec. They were up and turning back when we saw one drop and then another slanted down. The pop...pop of the shots drifted faintly to our ears.

The ebbing tide was taking the fallen birds away from us. Alec hadn't the benefit of a dog as Rosy was back in Norfolk, so I hurried along the bank sending Jet ahead. He was reluctant to go at first until he saw the distant figure of

Alec and then he soon bounded off, eager to play his part. Before I reached the spot, Jet was lolloping up the mudshelf with a duck held crossways in his soft mouth. Ignoring Alec he brought the fowl to me - it was a female pochard.

"Where's the other one?" I asked.

"Every time I've got anywhere near it, it dives," Alec replied. "There it is!" Seventy yards away was a vee-shaped ripple indicating a moving object in the water. With just the head showing above the surface, the stricken bird was making full use of the tide. Alec ran along the bank in another attempt to get into range. He managed it too, but as soon as the gun touched his shoulder the duck dived again and the pellets sprayed the spot where it had been. That was enough for the pochard; we saw no more sign of it. They can swim a long way underwater and with the assistance of the tide, it would have put a considerable distance between the hunter and the quarry in a short space of time. Regretfully we had to give it up as a lost bird.

We were still discussing this when shots from Tom echoed along the river. We could see him coming along the bank, eyes fixed on something in the water. I walked back towards him and could see a duck drifting on the tide in midstream. Jet saw it too and tore along the brink to a point nearby, launched himself and hit the water with a tremendous splash, well out from the bank. He brought in another pochard, a fine drake with a burnished red head. It was the first pochard that Tom had ever handled, let alone shot and the lad was absolutely delighted.

Resuming our stations we waited on, but nothing else offered a chance and those wigeon out on the ice obviously had no intention of moving. We called it a day and ambled back towards the car. In trying to analyse why the sport had been poor, we came to the conclusion that the weather conditions had been neither one thing nor the other. The frost had closed up most of the floodwater, but it had not been freezing long enough to fill the tidal river with fowl. Another two or three days for example, would have closed in deeper waters such as gravel pits and then there would at the very least, have been some good sport with pochard and tufted duck. Still, it had by no means been a blank, we had seen plenty and we were pleased for young Tom. As we climbed the bank, a cock pheasant almost took us by surprise as it burst out of the bleached rough grass under our feet. It veered left, long tail aquiver, but Alec dropped him onto the frosted sward twenty feet below us, where he lay still, a picture of red, gold and black.

Back at my house there was time to spare, so we decided to prepare some of the birds for the oven, retiring to my outbuildings where a few feathers adrift on the floor would be nothing out of the ordinary. The idea was to form a production line with two plucking and one drawing, but it transpired that Tom had never cleaned a bird or anything else for that matter. Living at home with his parents, any game was prepared by his mother.

"Well Tom," Alec said, "any sportsman worthy of the name should clean at least some of his bag and now is as good a time as any for you to learn. There's nothing to it."

To start with, we all took a wigeon each and sat around a large cardboard box, which very soon had a covering of feathers in the bottom. Tom watched and plucked his bird in stages, following our instructions and what we hoped were useful tips. We demonstrated how by plucking a small patch of the breast right to the skin and then by pushing your thumb firmly over the skin in a pinching movement towards the first finger, you can usually roll off the feathers and down in one action. We moved on to the back and the first inch of the wings closest to the body. Finally each bird was held by one leg at a time so that the body hung down, making it easier to pluck the legs and tail. Tom plucked his pochard drake while we tackled the female and the remaining two wigeon. When all the ducks were free of feathers, Alec took them over to the old stone sink and began to draw them, while I got Tom started on the pheasant.

I told him to pluck the back of the bird first, because even a novice can remove those feathers quite quickly without fear of tearing the skin. The same applied to the legs.

"You'll need to be a bit gentle with the breast on a pheasant Tom," I advised. "The skin there is easy to tear. Of course, some birds are already torn by brambles, or other cover when they fall, so it's not a disaster if you tear it - it looks better if you don't, that's all. Lay the bird on its side on your lap and brush the breast feathers upwards and you can see how most of the quills are in a band along the length of the breast. There, do you see?" Tom nodded so I went on.

"Sometimes it's best to pull those feathers almost singly at first until you see how it's going. With experience you will know what sort of bird you have got. This one seems pretty sound - I don't think it will tear. That's the way - you can hear the *rrrrrip* as you strip off each bunch of feathers. You can do such a bird, quite quickly. Yes, there will always be somebody who will tell you that they can prepare a pheasant or a partridge in so many seconds flat. Well that's fine as a party trick but otherwise you might as well take a bit of time over the job and finish with a presentable bird."

We went over to join Alec at the sink where he had used a stout pair of scissors to remove heads, wings and legs. The birds now lay in a neat row on the draining board behind a stack of pages torn from a broadsheet newspaper. Four of the wigeon had been cleaned and these reclined in a large baking tray.

"Now then Tom," said Alec, "you might not be looking forward to the next job, but I can tell you that this is the easy bit. You can have a go at the pheasant first. Put the bottom blade of the scissors into the vent and snip about an inch and a half up to the base of the breastbone - that's it. Now go to the throat and pull back and out the sac of skin full of wheat and seeds - that's the crop. Now carefully insert a finger into the throat cavity and run the finger round to loosen the innards. The heart and gullet pipe should come out with your finger. One thing to remember is to never ram your finger in carelessly because occasionally there are broken bones in there. These are obviously very sharp and jagged and for some reason a cut from them is sore for days.

"Right, now go back to the vent and stick your finger in until you feel a hard ball shape. That's the gizzard - the bird's digestive organ. Hook your finger round it and pull it back until you can get your thumb on the other side. Once you can grip it, pull firmly and steadily and most of the innards will come out in a mass onto your sheet of paper. There, see what I mean? Ok, now run the cold tap through the bird and feel for any stray bits and pieces that are left inside, there shouldn't be much. Now wash the body all over under the running tap to get rid of any flecks of feather or blood, then flush out the inside again - that's it. Now, push up the legs into the 'trussed chicken' shape and you have a very nice oven-ready pheasant and you got it ready yourself. Easy ain't it?"

Tom nodded his agreement.

"I never thought it would be so easy and it wasn't as messy as I thought it would be either," he grinned

"Now that's a lovely clean bird," Alec continued, "and the breast is unmarked because I shot him as he was flying away from me. All right, now try the pochard, I won't interfere unless you ask me to."

Tom set about cleaning the duck and had obviously been paying attention, for he completed it to all intents and purposes, on his own. Alec showed him how to pinch out the yellow fat deposits at the tail and gave the body a final rinse through. There were only two pellet holes in one side, otherwise it was as clean as the pheasant.

"They don't usually come as clean as that early in the season Tom," I cut in. "September mallard can be a bit of a menace with lots of quills and short down left in place after plucking. I've tried to singe them off with a lighted twist of newspaper or even with a blowlamp - it does the job but it's not really satisfactory. Apparently you can dip the whole bird in wax for a clean finish, but I've not tried that."

"Did you notice Tom, that the blood of the diving ducks seems to be thicker than that of the surface feeders? Alec chimed in. "I'll tell you something else, the pochard's eyes are red and the tufted duck's eyes are yellow. I don't know if is anything to do with giving them better vision underwater, but I've wondered about it for some time now."

I handed a wigeon to Tom.

"This is the last one. Do you want to do it?"

Tom nodded and got down to the task. Alec and I were arranging the finished birds in tin trays, ready to go into the refrigerator, but we were surreptitiously watching Tom. We did not have to wait long.

"This is different!" He said. "I haven't seen one of these in the other birds."

He was holding the small spherical protrusion attached to the gullet pipe of the drake wigeon.

"Well spotted Tom!" smiled Alec. "I'm pretty sure that the whistling call of the drake wigeon is produced from that little gristle globe. I have asked a wildfowl expert, but he couldn't confirm that, or my theory about the eyes. He just said both ideas were possible. Anyway, you've had enough lessons for one day. Hurry up and finish that one off so we can get cleaned up - it's almost lunch time."

The winter afternoons being short, we did not allow much time for post lunch digestion. I was keen to get us a couple of hours after pheasants. I might have said game, but I knew that it was a lucky man who got anywhere near a walked-up partridge at this time of year. We were to shoot on my friend Jack's farm, which we last visited in October. Fortunately, the drive to the farm would not take up much of our time. I parked the car just off the hard road on a muddy grass drove lined with a row of poplar trees on one side. We crossed the road and lined out to walk some ploughed land. There was one field that had been late-harvested sugar beet and this had not yet been ploughed. Most of the other land had been. There was even some even drilling, the thin green rows of winter wheat showed clearly against the rich black mixture of peat and clay. Where the land had been drilled, we kept off it and walked on either side of the boundary dykes. Almost all of the dykes were dry with a thick growth of brown rushes and grasses grey-white where the sap had run back to the roots. On this still frosty day, most of the birds would be here, sheltering from a keen little wind. Jet thoroughly enjoyed himself working and snuffling through the cover. Sometimes all that could be seen was the movement of the grasses and then his grinning black face would thrust through to make sure we were still there. If he stopped and pushed his head forward into the cover it gave us a bit of a warning that he might be about to flush a pheasant, but when birds clattered out thirty yards ahead of the dog they usually took us by surprise. Due to the restrictions of all walking together along the dykes, we took it in turns to take the first shot. Once, when it was Tom's turn to shoot, there was a terrific fluttering and scrambling giving the lad ample time to get ready... then out flew a moorhen, low and straight. Tom threw up his gun, realised his mistake, and almost tied himself in knots attempting to hold his fire. Alec and I were chuckling, but we did not let on that the bird had fooled us, too.

Many hundred yards of dyke were walked without finding game, but nevertheless we had five pheasants in our bags when we found ourselves near Jack's pick-up truck. Its owner had been drilling wheat and was in the process of parking his tractor on a grass headland for the night. He climbed down from the cab and walked over to us.

"Har ye done any good?" he asked. "I've had plenty of pheasants running in front of me all day, but that's often the case when you are on a tractor ain't it? They don't take any notice of you. It's a different matter if you step down for a minute."

We told him that we had enjoyed some sport and he seemed pleased with the brace offered to him. As we stood talking about how his harvest had been and of how things were changing in the fen he glanced up.

"Look, here comes my old dog. She's seen me park up the tractor and she knows that means I'm going home. She's coming so that she can ride home in the truck with me. They're not stupid are they?" Two fields away a border collie could be seen running towards us. She cleared a dry dyke with an effortless bound that did not break her stride, disappeared for a moment below the brink of a deep water-filled main dyke, jumped it, climbed out and shook, before coming on the home straight to master who rubbed her head affectionately when she eventually arrived.

We left them and walked across a ploughed field towards the drove where the car stood. A good covey of partridges flew from the far end of the field, a quarter mile away. By now many of the coveys had broken up into breeding pairs; in fact the only other partridges we had seen had been a pair, which flushed equally as wild as the covey. On the grass drove we kept an eye on Jet as he went from the deep rough dyke on one side, to the line of trees and shrubs on the other.

"Watch him," I warned, "there's been something along here fairly recently - look at his tail." Nose down and his rudder doing it's best to imitate the stubby tail of an excited spaniel, Jet was going this way and that among the ground cover below the trees. Suddenly the trail straightened out and Jet was off like a train, vanishing under a bush. From the other side, a cock pheasant shot out, crowing in defiance and anger. Unluckily for him, Tom had walked up that side of the trees. Although the bird was forty yards away and climbing fast, the youth brought him down with a cracking shot. Jet steamed off to retrieve and came back with the bird, wearing what seemed like a smug self-satisfied expression that said - "You can rely on me chaps, I'll find 'em for you!"

Alec and Tom had to leave as soon as we got back to my house, so we shared out the duck from the refrigerator and of course that day's bag. I gave Tom a brace of pheasants including that last cock bird.

"There you are, now you can surprise your parents by showing them that you can clean and prepare your birds for the roasting tin."

30

January 26

Somehow, within the past nine days, the authorities controlling the drainage system had managed to discharge a fair amount of floodwater from the washlands into the tidal river, despite the fact that the tides were high following the new moon. We could only surmise that the water running from higher ground had become a spent force. However it had been achieved, it had the effect of reducing water levels over a considerable area of the washes. This was good for us because it left large pools, and plenty of grass showing to draw down the wigeon.

The old Ford nosed into my drive quite early on that Friday afternoon with Alec keen as mustard to make the most of the flooding on this last weekend of the inland season. If it were possible, he became even more enthusiastic because there was half a gale blowing from the southwest. It took me all of my time to persuade him to come into the house for a break after his journey; I think he was worried in case the wind abated before we were out with our guns. My wife prevailed upon him by saying that she had made a pot of tea especially for his arrival. I managed to get his overnight bag into the house, but I could tell from his anxious glances towards the window that my friend was not going to relax until we were on our way. So, much to Jet's approval, we got ready and went.

Once more my poor car was put to the test along the muddy drove on the washlands. The mud had a reddish tinge, because beneath the gravelled surface and in the potholes the track had been made up with brickbats. After driving as far as we could, before the track turned to mud and nothing but mud we left the car and embarked on the long walk. The floodwater had gone from the drove except for some large puddles, but each field had its pools or more extensive sheets of water, framed by rectangles of grass. I explained to Alec that when the dykes have been cleaned out over the years, the mud and rushes had been spread along the sides of the watercourses. Over time this had built them up slightly higher than the middle of the fields. This suited the likes of us, because it meant that the water lingered longer. The owners of the land were not particularly bothered for they accepted that this was a flood plain. However, if the water remained on the surface come spring, with the grazing season approaching, they would take a spade and cut grips for the water to run off more quickly. I pointed out more than one such a grip, as we ambled along the headlands of the field we had earmarked for our flight.

The dyke sides were well grown up with rushes, thistles and willow herb so wherever we decided to wait; we could be assured of ample cover. We chose our spots, eighty yards apart and trod down the vegetation like a couple of dogs making their beds after clean new straw has been piled in their kennel. Mock not, they made good hides and kept out at least some of the wind. The wind... Yes it was blowing strongly all right. Alec joined me to share a flask of coffee and produced his pipe. Tapping it out on his palm, he filled it with Gold Block from his pouch and then patted his pockets to locate his matches. This was an action of habit for he knew very well which pocket held his Vestas and it wasn't his cartridge pocket!

I decided to join him and filled my pipe from his pouch before he could put it away. Then came the problem of lighting up in a strong wind. In time-honoured fashion Alec stood hunched, back to the wind, his pipe shielded as much as possible inside his jacket front. I'm not sure how it happened, but somehow he managed to open his box too far so that the wind scooped out what matches it contained and scattered them all over the water. Alec's face was a picture; I thought for one second I was about to see a grown man cry. I laughed and with a flourish pulled out my Zippo, windproof lighter.

"You want to get yourself one of these old son," I grinned. "They'll not let you down in any…"

My voice trailed off as I repeatedly flicked the wheel against the flint.

"Always provided that they have been topped up with flipping lighter fuel!" snorted Alec, with an unwarranted hint of sarcasm I thought.

A low flying teal saved me from further embarrassment as Alec scuttled back to his hide, pipes and tobacco forgotten for the time being.

That teal was a lone wanderer, however, and although we were now on the alert no more of his brothers came to tempt us, at least not until dusk. Then, as if by magic, the place became alive. From one direction, duck came in like the proverbial bats out of hell; from the other, they seemed hardly to make any progress against the wind. For all that, most of the fowl were far too high for our magnums. As the light faded, lapwings came swirling, tumbling and twisting between us and all about us. They were very low indeed, their wings making a ripping sound. Teal did fly lower, many of them at head height. They seemed to rely on their speed and were justified in their confidence. I think we both missed more than we hit, but they did not all get by. As usual it was almost too dark to see when the wigeon made their move, but what exciting moments when they did. Wave after wave, line upon line and company after company swept over us on a front several hundred yards broad. There were frenzied bursts of whistling and growling, but it was the fantastic tearing and rush of two thousand pairs of flickering wings that made the heart leap. Most of them were invisible against the dark eastern sky, but some showed for a fraction of time and more than once I threw up the gun only to bring it down again as the hurtling shape was quickly lost from sight. In a brief lull between waves I spotted a moving blurred shape heading for Alec's hide. I could see the duck was because it was flying lower than the massed ranks of wigeon, but I wondered if Alec had noticed it. I need not have concerned myself; there was a sharp report followed by a vision of the shape suddenly falling to earth. It went down beyond the dyke behind us. Jet almost cleared the dyke in one mighty bound and after splashing around for a bit he returned with a mallard. Even in the poor light, the drake's white 'clerical' collar showed as a clear demarcation between the dark head and breast. He was in prime condition as I commented to Alec when handing the bird over. One final rush of sound and the last of the wigeon hordes had gone to their feed, wherever that might be.

Now that night had fallen, the wind had definitely lost its power and as we sloshed homewards along the drove it was possible to hear other fowl on the move. A line of Bewick's swans flew up, mildly whooping to each other to maintain contact. Then…

"Hark! I thought I heard…"

"I heard them too," said Alec.

"There they are again - pinks!"

We dived unnecessarily into a gateway, fumbling for some heavily loaded cartridges. Now the calling of the geese was regular, unimpeded by the wind and becoming louder. They were coming towards us! We might just see them against the sky if they came low enough. The pinkfeet suddenly went quiet - where the devil are they? Are they still coming? Have they landed? All these thoughts went through my mind in the seconds that followed. Then came the 'creak, creak' of large wings beating a steady rhythm. We knew that for us to hear that creak the geese must be very close indeed. So close, but not a glimpse did we get.

When we had settled in the car, before switching on the ignition, I turned towards Alec.

"How are you now then? Are you suffering from withdrawal symptoms?"

"I'll get over it," Alec grunted. "But if you'd remembered to refill that damned lighter…"

I reached over to the glove compartment, pulled out a box of matches and handed it over without a word. It wasn't long before, with a face wreathed in smiles, Alec had thoroughly fumigated the interior of my car.

31

January 27

The wind fell away completely during the night allowing thick cloud to form. The darkness felt more oppressive than usual when Alec and I made our way once more along the muddy drove the next morning. This particular drove runs straight as an arrow though the middle of the washlands. In summertime the walking is easy as a rule, the grass track having been baked hard by days of unbroken sunshine. Now in its mid-winter state, quite the opposite was true, with sodden grass and mud, and the water table barely beneath the surface of the land. The only time walking at this time of the year can be described as good is when the drove has been gripped by two or three days of continuous frost.

We squelched along, keeping one ear cocked for the sounds of awakening wildfowl. Not for the first time, we marvelled how quickly the shooting season passes by. We have hardly settled into it before Christmas is upon us and after Christmas, well it's all over almost before you can blink an eye. It is an altogether different matter when waiting impatiently for August to pass. The grouse shooters have a two-week start of course, but not many wildfowlers are counted among those privileged shooting parties. During those dog days of summer, the time seems to pass so slowly for the men who wait for September first.

The low cloud continued to press down like an enormous quilted mattress attempting to preserve the modesty of the first light of the dawning, which strove to reveal itself to all and sundry. After striding along for a mile-and-a-half, I stopped near a field gate to remove six duck decoys from the sack I was carrying. I then handed the sack to Alec, I pointing out a gateway visible two fields further on.

"Go into that field and you'll find a decent flash of water. I've left some 'coys in the sack for you. When you've set them out, you can hang the sack on the barbed wire fence to give you a bit of a hide, but make use of any available natural cover too. I'm going to try my hand in here - see you later, g'luck!"

Nodding his agreement, Alec hefted the sack and moved on along the drove while I set off across the wash towards the flash I fancied. All of the pools and flashes looked as though they ought to be attractive to duck, but it was by no means always the case.

Jet and I splashed our way through the soggy grasses between coarse spiky tussocks. One or two snipe sprang up, scraping a protest as they flitted away unseen in the unrelenting gloom. Gloom or not, birds were waking up, as distant whistles and muted quacks testified. I had better get a move on. The chosen spot was at the edge of a pool, one-hundred-and-fifty yards from the bank of the tidal river. Quickly gathering an armful of dead and brittle willow herb and nettle stalks from the side of a nearby dyke, I jabbed the sharp broken ends into the soft peat to form a natural looking butt with room for both me and the dog. Some handfuls of pale and washed out dead grass, strewn and woven among the upright stems completed the picture. Just so long as I could prevent Jet from leaning against it, all would be well. I set out my six mallard decoys and watched as they swung this way and that, tugging at their lead-weighted cords. They looked fine to me. I hoped that the duck would share my confidence in them.

When first light finally managed to break through, a fine rain began to contribute to the already waterlogged scene. It might have been impatience on my part, but this did seem to delay the flight even more. Before long, however, there was no doubt that morning had broken. A raucous quacking from a mallard duck as she stretched up and flapped her wings in response to some inner body clock came to my ears. Although she was out of sight, I had witnessed this little ritual so many times that I could picture her in my mind's eye as though she was right there on the water in front of me. A small team of duck, already on the wing, chuckled to each other as they headed off to spend the day in some quiet corner of the fen. They would have been feeding overnight, perhaps on rotting potatoes between the rows of newly emerging winter wheat. At around one o'clock in the morning they would have flown into the washes to swill off the mud from their feet and plumage, before dozing off on the water, secure from foxes and other predators. Now they were on the move again.

Prrrrp, Prrrrp. Pintail, or at least one drake was on the move. From another direction a rush of wings and a hurtling black shape, seen and gone in the twinkling of an eye. Then came a mass of wigeon that whistled and growled overhead. Long arcs and strings of speeding duck passed, so exciting to watch, but far too high to even consider raising the gun. In fact it was almost light before my first real chance presented itself. A lone duck approached not high, but passing wide. A very long white neck made the dark head appear to fly a foot in front of the body, and instantly identified the bird as a pintail drake. It had passed by as I gave it a call on my wigeon whistle, the brass heads of two eight-bore cartridges pressed one into the other, and the drake pivoted round to fly back, but just as wide of me. Another whistle and back he came once more, but this time near enough for my shot to fold him up. Before the bird had hit the water, Jet charged off after it and whilst watching him I was taken by surprise, by the sound of rapidly beating wings. Looking to the front, I was in time to see a pochard drake climbing wildly from over the decoys. It was obvious that he was dropping into them when, at the last moment he had spotted me. He was still well within range, enabling me to send him crashing into the floodwater before Jet had returned with the pintail.

A good start indeed, but it wasn't to last. I was frustrated and humbled by a series of unexplainable misses at teal. Worse still, as a spring of a dozen came buzzing round, I hit one, which carried on momentarily before gliding steeply down onto the brink of the far side of the river. The dog had not seen it go down but went across willingly to search. He came back without the bird and I began to wonder if it had recovered and flown off while I was out of sight. I sent Jet over again, further downwind this time. He hunted around for some time until I had almost given it up as a lost bird when suddenly, down went his head and he had it. Well done Jet!

The flight was over by now, so I gathered up the decoys and bag with the intention of intercepting Alec who was making his way towards me. Funnily enough, I had been so engrossed in my own activities that I had not heard him shooting. Nevertheless, he had been shooting and was carrying a couple of wigeon and a female pintail. We had a good variety of duck this morning and no mistake. We had ended the inland wildfowl shooting season on a high note and even though the rain followed us all the way back to the car there was no way it could dampen our spirits.

32

February 2

Darkness had overtaken us before Alec's arrival, so we had supper and prepared for a quiet evening. Later, Jet wanted to go outside to his kennel and when I went with him, I was greeted by the most glorious moonlit sky. I called Alec to come and look.

"You rarely get a sky like that when you want one," he said.

We stood in the driveway admiring the small white clouds backlit by her lunar majesty and a thought struck me.

"It may sound silly, but do you fancy a drive down to the washes, just for a look round?"

"You know," replied Alec, "that's a good idea, it's still early. Yes, I do fancy it."

I quickly made a flask of coffee and told my wife of our intentions. She was used to the strange hours kept by wildfowlers and simply said that she preferred to stay by the fire and might be in bed before we returned.

In due course we were splashing and lurching along the gravelled drove, taking an erratic course to avoid the majority of the potholes. Leaving the car at last, we walked out into a splendid night of fresh crisp air with a touch of frost. Almost at once we heard wigeon and more than a few. We heard one bunch of teal as they made their way downriver, talking to one another as they sped along in search of some fresh feed. Bewick's swans came whooping overhead in long angled lines, each huge bird in the slipstream of the one in front, as they headed for a noisy gathering of their tribe on water further along the wash. In fact, the usual silence of the washlands was replaced with the various calls of wildfowl; quacks, whistles, whoops, growls, and pipes that emulated from flashes and pools and from all quarters, while the air above and around us hissed and buzzed with wings. As it turned out, we did not actually see that many, but enough to have made for first class flight, had we been armed.

"Isn't it funny? This would never happen if we had a gun in our hands," chuckled Alec.

We wandered further along the drove and then across to the riverbank, where we found the tide at a low ebb and the slopes of the extensive mud-shelves still wet and shining in the moonlight. Looking down from the relative height of the bank afforded us a good position from which to observe the dozens of pools and splashes of floodwater, each one easily seen due the moon's reflected light. We walked some distance along the bank and finally came to the larger area of water, upon which the swans had chosen to roost. These big birds were bulky enough to be seen and we identified a gathering of about two hundred Bewick's with a score of mutes swimming a little way off from them. As our eyes adjusted to the unusual light we could even discern a dark smudge that was a raft of wigeon, watched with glasses as they moved slowly but surely towards the grassy fringes.

After another hour the pace of events slowed somewhat, but there was still the occasional movement of fowl. However, we decided that we had satisfied the primeval urge to be out under such a moon and so descended the bank to make our way back to the drove. At the base of the bank and spreading out into the field, was a substantial area of thick grasses and rushes, which brushed noisily against our boots as we pushed through the cover. About ten paces into it, the ground all around our feet erupted as at least a dozen pheasants whirred up with an almighty racket, making us both jump.

"My Godfathers!" laughed Alec when we had recovered from the sudden shock. "Your old pheasants don't half sit tight, that's the second time this season they've nearly finished me off!"

The last thing we heard as we closed the car doors for the drive home was a company of wigeon whistling away as they flew along, following the drove into the great silence of the night.

Naturally, we did not bother to rise very early in the morning and after a late breakfast, settled down to plucking what remained of my share of last week's bag. When that job was done and dusted, we drove to Jack and Sally's farm to present them with some bottles of the good stuff as a gesture of thanks for another season's sport. Typically, they could not bring themselves to accept the gift without returning the compliment and so at their insistence, we had to pick up a bag of potatoes as we passed the store shed.

We spent the afternoon dozing in front of the fire for we knew that we would be in for another late night out under the moon. We dreamed of perfect skies and thousands of geese in vees, lines and echelons all heading straight for us. Of how every shot told, and we began to be anxious as to how we should carry home all the fallen. Of course, that sort of thing never happens on the foreshore in real life and it's a good job that it doesn't. Nevertheless, it is the hopes and dreams of the flight of a lifetime that fires the enthusiasm. Could this be the night? In three or four hours time we would find out.

Before we reached the hard standing at the base of the sea wall, the headlights picked up the shapes of two cars already parked there.

"Blast! I wonder where they've gone?" muttered Alec, somewhat unreasonably. We wildfowlers are always jealous of our special places and see any intrusion by others as trespass out of all proportion. I have no doubt that those already out on the marsh muttered similar maledictions under their breath at the sight of our approaching lights. We pulled up beside the other cars and had a quick look to see if we recognised them.

"I reckon that's old Smithy's Vauxhall, I've seen it at Cley," growled Alec, beginning to resemble a pugnacious Jack Russell. "I'll bet a pound to a pinch of marsh mud, that old bugger knows where the geese are coming in to feed."

"Well," I replied. "There's plenty of room down here so let's get cracking. It was high tide around four o'clock so that will be well out now. We don't have to worry about that if we go out onto the marsh, but for the time being I think we ought to stay on the sea wall. Then if we hear geese we can run towards the first lot that comes off."

"Yes, I agree," said my friend. " I'll cut along for about half a mile then we will cover a good frontage between us. Don't shoot 'em all!" With that he was gone, clumping along at a fair rate of knots in his hurry to beat the moon. The sound of his footsteps gradually faded and I was left alone with my thoughts. The moon was already rising and as she continued her ascent, more and more of my surroundings were lit with that pale soft light. Yet there were no clouds. The wind was offshore, which meant the geese would have to fly into it, but I doubted whether it was strong enough to bother those powerful fowl. It might be strong enough to blow up some clouds for us, but it would have to make haste because there was now sufficient light to tempt a hungry pinkfoot back to the fields inland.

Within five minutes, no more, I heard one lot come in, but they passed between Alec and me. I ran along the track behind the seawall as fast as I could in thigh boots and heavy clothing. Again the sound of geese on the move could be heard. I stopped to listen, mouth open, one ear to the wind. How quickly the sound of their calling passed over the unseen salt-marsh. Boom! Boom! I hurried on towards the sound of the shots. I came across Alec sooner than I had expected. He was crouched among the crab grass below the wall.

"That wasn't me shooting," he said, in reply to my yet unspoken question. "He's up there about another two hundred yards. I'll bet it's old Smithy."

"He's using a heavy gun by the sound of it, whoever it is," I commented.

"That last lot sounded pretty high," said Alec. "Shall we try to get out to the stalk edges before the next lot come? They might be lower until they see the saltings underneath them."

"It's worth a try," I agreed. "They seem to be coming off along here." We strode through the marsh with the crab grass brushing our boots, stumbling in the little gutters it concealed, hopping over the narrow ones we saw in time and generally skidding our way to the edge of the marsh. We were almost there when we were stopped in our tracks by the sound of a third skein approaching. We dropped down onto one knee and stared at the space ahead of us. Wink! Wink! Wiwink! Surely this lot were coming straight for us? These were exciting, heart-thumping moments as we strained our eyes for a sighting. No, they were passing us now, and then for a fraction of a second I saw the skein against a patch of white cloud. The geese must have been eighty yards away, but it is hard to judge in that light. We listened to see if the gunner on the sea bank was in luck again, but the calling faded into the distance uninterrupted by the sudden blast of a shot.

Hang on a minute - a cloud? I saw the geese against a cloud! I turned and there was the cloud and behind it a massive bank of the white fluffy stuff that gladdens the heart of the moonlight shooter. Slowly, oh so slowly, the cloudbank crept towards the moon. Soon the whole velvet sky was transformed into a beautifully patterned backdrop of soft white, with the moon vanishing and reappearing like an exotic fan dancer in a Parisian nightclub. We feared that it had arrived just too late for no more skeins came crying in. All the same, it was a lovely night and a joy to be out enveloped in its magic. We stood where the salt-marsh merged into the glistening mud, taking in the scene and marvelling at the silvery sheen on all the little pools of water.

"Sssh! Listen," Alec blurted out.

I listened and heard nothing, but then a familiar steady, rhythmic creaking sound came to my ears.

"It's a pink - and he must be very close," I said. "Give him a call."

Alec put his fingers in his mouth and gave a loud buzzing whistle - Wiwink! There was no answering call, but the creaking was coming nearer again. The goose must have circled us.

"There it is!" choked Alec as he swung up his magnum. I looked up and there was the goose, silhouetted black against that glorious cloud cover. Alec fired and for a split second I thought he had missed, but the goose wasn't moving forwards anymore. It's neck and wings were still outstretched and I was puzzled at what had happened. I then realised that the huge shape was getting larger - it was parachuting down! All of a sudden the air spilled from one wing and the great bird tumbled to hit the marsh not ten feet from us. Alec had only to step three paces to pick the goose, which appeared to be completely unmarked by pellets. It was even clean, having fallen onto stiff crab grass rather than the mud.

"Well, that was stroke of luck!" Alec exclaimed. "It must have somehow got parted from the skein and was trying to find them. These lone geese will usually respond to a call and will even fly right over you in broad daylight.

"Yes," I replied. "I shot my first goose in thick fog. A little party of pinkfeet, obviously lost, came out of the fog no more than head height. They were right on top of me and as I only had time for one hurried shot, I was lucky to pull one down."

We waited a while longer, but the geese had all gone in to the fields and no more creaking wings thrilled us that night, even though the cloud background was still perfect. As we clambered up the sea wall to leave the marsh, we heard the sound of voices approaching, so we waited until two shadowy figures hove into sight. It wasn't old Smithy despite Alec's speculation, but two wildfowlers from the Midlands. One of them hefted a mighty double-barrelled eight-bore over his shoulder and hanging down his back, suspended from the barrels of the gun, we discerned the bulky shape of a goose.

"You got among 'em then?" invited Alec.

"Aye, we did an' all," replied Eight-Bore. "Well, I did. They were too far out for you weren't they Albert? There must have been about thirty in the skein, I couldn't see them very well. It were afore the cloud came up. They were pretty high too, but this old gel 'ull fetch 'em. If the sky had been as good as it is now, I reckon I'd have had a right and left, no trouble."

We all walked back to the cars together, during which time we told them of Alec's lucky goose and in turn we discovered that the pair had first visited the marsh as part of a coach-load of shooters from Leicester, who had employed Mackenzie Thorpe as their guide. As we deposited our gear into the back of the car, I inspected Alec's goose with the aid of a torch. I found that a single pellet of BB had gone through the chin and out through the top of the head. No wonder it froze in mid-flight. Obviously, I pointed this out to Alec.

"Unless you find any more pellets when you pluck it, that was a fluke of a shot and a very unlucky goose."

"Noo…Noo!" came the retort. "Sheer good shooting that was. Sheer good shooting - nothing less."

33

February 17

Rhymes that relate to weather lore differ slightly depending on the locality, but as far as I know 'February fill dyke, fill it black or fill it white' is known and used throughout the kingdom. Well, this particular year the dykes were filled with the white stuff. After one or two false starts, winter had decided to make it's presence felt and there had been a good covering of some four or five inches of snow, after which the frost had set in for a couple of days. Then came a slight rise in the temperature, which triggered a further fall of snow. Although the conditions on the main roads were far from ideal, they were passable. Whilst flooding occasionally prevents the passage of motorcars in parts of fenland, it is rare for fen roads to become blocked with snow. Being slightly higher than the flat surrounding fields the wind blows the snow from the roads and nature keeps the highway clear. Having that knowledge borne of experience, I was not surprised to see the old Ford Popular come chugging down the road that Friday afternoon.

What did mildly surprise me, was what happened next. The car scrunched to a halt in my drive whereupon a strange apparition struggled out, stretched erect and shook itself like a bear. Alec looked twice his normal size muffled up as he was with scarf, cap, thick gloves and several layers of sweaters topped off with a heavy ex-army great coat.

"You know, anybody would think it was cold," I laughed.

From behind the folds of his scarf Alec mumbled.

"You would never believe the draughts that come through the floor of the old bus and you'd believe even less where they get too. I'm bloody perished!"

"We'd better get you thawed out then," I said, trying hard to control further laughter. "I'll bring your bags in. You get inside quick, there's a good fire in the living room that will bring you back to life without a doubt."

Alec did not hesitate, but made for the back door at once. With his holdall in one hand and his gun in the other, I pushed my way through the door. There he stood in front of the glowing hearth, shedding coat and sweaters into my wife's waiting arms. She was giggling as she went to hang up the coat. Poor old Alec, he wasn't getting much sympathy from any quarter. Even the cat that had been unceremoniously dislodged from the hearthrug to make way for our shivering guest, sat glaring like an owl at the intruder.

After toasting - almost roasting - himself on all sides until his trousers showed signs of scorching, our friend was back to his old self and on top leg-pulling form. The heat thrown out by the fire was too much for Jet, who had retreated to a more comfortable position near my chair. Now that he was satisfied that we were not going shooting this evening, he lay snoring contentedly.

With road conditions unlikely to be showing much improvement in the morning, we loaded what we could, such as boots and side-bags into my car. We also loaded a brace of shovels and some old hessian potato sacks. In this weather one never knew when they might be needed.

As it was, when we ventured out in the morning, the main roads did not seem too bad. Where other traffic had been, the snow had been churned into grimy brown slush that sprayed outwards from beneath the wheels. Due to the lack of traffic, the nearer we got to the Lincolnshire coast, the worse the roads became, until we were driving on top of tightly packed snow. Even this was all right so long as one managed to keep to a reasonably straight course and did not, in any circumstances, apply the brakes. More than once, we felt the rear end of the car drifting sideways on bends with a mind of its own, but it soon followed when we straightened up again.

At the marsh entrance there was an old wartime pillbox, known by hundreds of wildfowlers. The brickwork was covered with snow rendering it all but invisible against the beginnings of the sea wall. With invisibility in mind, Alec and I had years before, made ourselves snow camouflage smocks. I had simply folded an old once white, woollen blanket in half and drawn a T- shaped outline on it. The outline was then cut out with scissors and the halves crudely sewn together. The hole for the head was slit down the front, to make the smock easier to get on. Three pairs of holes were punched down the sides of the slit and one of those long football bootlaces was inserted. The smocks were designed to be worn over the usual wildfowling clothing, including the waterproof jacket, so the final touch was to cut slits to allow access to pockets and cartridges. Had we been endowed with tailoring skills we might have added a hood, but instead we made do with grey or off-white woollen hats. I hasten to add that these were knitted without the embellishment of either pom-poms or bobbles!

The whiteness of the smocks emphasised the black of our thigh boots, but when we knelt in the snow we were fairly invisible. Moreover, being woollen, our homemade outfits gave us added warmth. I once own a pair of sheepskin mitts that were really warm, but taking a shot necessitated the swift removal of the right hand mitt. This meant that every time this happened the mitt could be dropped into water or lost in the snow. To get around this minor problem I linked the mitts on a long tape, which ran from the left mitt, up the sleeve, around the neck and down the other sleeve to the right hand mitt. Just like a toddler in his first pair of gloves. It worked though; I could slip off the mitten, which would hang below my sleeve until I had taken the shot. As in the case of other items of shooting kit, improved and better quality gloves would eventually make it unnecessary to resort to such measures.

That, however, was yet to come, and so for the time being we donned our white smocks and commenced the long walk along the sea bank. The reflected light from the snowy landscape meant that it was never really dark, and this definitely made the walking easier. Jet was highly delighted and bounded about, playing like child in the snow, turning every now and again to check that we were still coming. The walk out across the salt-marsh, when the time came, was a very different matter. The larger creeks and channels could be seen, but the snow had levelled out the smaller gutters. By that I mean visually, not physically. It was like walking over a minefield, never sure if your foot would go down on firm ground or if your leg would vanish up to the thigh in snow.

"We'd better go steady here," Alec cautioned, "or one of us will end up with a broken leg."

High water had been about half-past-three and there had been three hours of ebb, so as soon as it was practical we slid down into a large creek and waded along the bottom. The new moon was due in about three or four days and although the tides were building up, they were still not covering much of the green marsh. We came to the mark of this morning's tide, sharply defined black on one side, and white on the other. This was as far as we were going, because we wanted to hide in the good cover provided by the snow. There was hardly any wind to assist us, so we hoped that the lack of any green marsh in view might confuse the geese into flying low over it. We were not very optimistic, but as this was our last day on the coast this season, we had to accept the weather on offer and hope for the best. That is part of the magic of wildfowling, the unexpected can happen and often does.

Two-hundred-and-fifty yards apart, we hid in a landscape that could almost be mistaken for a polar scene. It was cold, but not bitterly so. In fact after I had stamped down the snow in a gutter and sat on it's edge using my bag as a cushion, I found that it became marginally warmer. The snow, banked up against the crab grass and spartina had created a useful windbreak. A brief flare followed by a tiny orange glow told me that Alec had sought solace in his pipe and tobacco. I marvelled, not for the first time, at the distance that a pinprick of light can be seen.

It became obvious that the comfort of my shelter did not extend to other parts of the foreshore. All was very still and quiet. The few birds we saw in the early half-light seemed generally lethargic. Yet the sunrise was splendid with shafts of alternate pale and dark grey light, projected fan-like through a wash of pastel greens and greys, until the approaching sun tinged the undersides of the clouds with rose pink. The sun hove into view from behind a bank of cloud along the horizon, a clear indication of winds to come later in the day. As the sun touched and lit our snowy world, so the first skein of pinkfeet lifted from far out on distant sands, and came thrashing in. A hundred or so grey shapes in perfect formation came right over me at least two gunshots high. Such was the light, that every pinion in those wide wings was clearly defined. They had hardly passed when more lifted and then more still, until the whole horizon to seaward was a mass of geese. Geese strung out in lines, bunching and stretching out once again. A good four thousand came in across a half-mile front, and more could be seen further down the shore. The sound of their calling thrilled us to the core and we drank it all in. It is part and parcel of the fowler's life, but one can never get enough of it. Every bird was well up out of harm's way, but there was no wind and even the youngsters had a season of experience behind them now. We had no regrets though; they had given us a wonderful spectacle. It had been worth making our difficult journey, which of course, was nothing compared to the travels of wild geese.

Having decided that all the geese had come in, Alec was making his way slowly back to the creek, so I followed suit and we reached it more or less simultaneously. We stopped for a breather and watched the geese flying up and down over the snow-covered fields beyond the sea wall.

"They can't find any food," said Alec. They'll be off further inland before long and if this snow doesn't thaw in a day or two, they'll clear off altogether."

"I don't know about the geese," I replied, "but I think we should clear off to our own feeding ground - I could eat a horse!"

The only real difference between our earlier journey and the homeward drive was that the latter was made in the hours of daylight enabling us to see where we were skidding. With care and common sense there was nothing to it. We simply took our time until we reached the clearer main roads, arriving home at about eleven o'clock. The familiar routine followed - drying off the dog and providing him with a handful of biscuits and a dish of warm, sweet milky tea. Next we took down, dried off and cleaned the guns and then and only then, we saw to our own comfort. A steaming hot bath with, in my case at least, water up to the neck. A late breakfast-cum-lunch and a pint of hot tea to thaw our chilled bones, put us in the right frame of mind to spend a relaxing three hours dozing in the armchairs beside the fire.

At half-past-two in the afternoon, we set out rather sheepishly to a marsh on the west Norfolk coast of The Wash, near the border with Lincolnshire. After this morning it was a rather forlorn hope, but as Alec pointed out, yet again, it was our last outing of the wildfowling season. So for the second time that day we tackled the snow-covered roads, again finding the last leg of the journey difficult. There were only two sets of wheel ruts in the snow on that narrow little road across acres of reclaimed land, one down and the other back. I kept our wheels in the ruts and drove along in third gear, until at last we fetched up under the sea wall. Then it was on with the snow camouflage smocks and long boots and a swift scramble up the side of the sea wall.

Alec was ahead of me and stopped on the top looking like Sherpa Tensing on the summit of Mount Everest. I joined him and together we surveyed the scene below. To say it was desolate would be an understatement. The snow had been a great leveller and on the now, reasonably flat, white surface a biting little wind sent grains of frozen snow scurrying and zigzagging before it, in much the same way as sand blows across a desert. It was just about on high tide and the waters were lapping the snowy bulwark halfway out across the saltings.

There were no waders around but there were a few wigeon swimming through the flooded grasses on the outer fringes of the marsh. This morning we had gone out in darkness, but now in daylight the place looked distinctly uninviting. For all that, we hadn't made the journey to stand and stare from the sea bank, so as the tide receded we pushed out as far as we could, moving on again when the dropping water level allowed. Dusk crept upon us before we had got to the edge of the snow and we heard the geese arrive, fresh from the fields. They didn't come over us, but we would not have fired if they had. With the wind behind them, these birds were well up in the sky. Long wavering lines called joyously as they passed by to begin their gradual descent to ride on the waves, and await the baring of the sands as the tide continued its ebb, miles out into The Wash.

As is their nature, the wigeon waited on until well after dark before they made an appearance, and even then, they were very quiet about it. I heard just one whistle warning me of an approaching pack, but they passed unseen on the dark side of me and the only indication of their passing was the rush of rapidly beating wings. They sounded low enough. A single shot rang out from Alec's direction and I wondered if he had scored. When we got together a little over fifteen minutes later, he told me that the same thing had happened to him and he had attempted to swing in front of the sound. I had heard of a similar practice used by wildfowlers flight-shooting on the marshes around Breydon Water, near Great Yarmouth. They occasionally met with success, whereas my companion this evening did not.

Our walk back along the sea wall was interrupted by the arrival of a late skein of pinkfeet. We stood in silence, savouring the thrilling sound until our ears could no longer pick it up. It was a fitting moment on which end the season. The memory was slightly marred when I reversed the car to drive out onto the road I ran us off the hard and into some deep snow. When I tried to drive forward the wheel spun ineffectually. Damn and Blast! At least three miles from the nearest habitation, this was not the place to be stuck. Alec pushed as I engaged the bottom gear, but to no avail. It was time to resort to the shovels and seed potato sacks. What a good thing we had thought to bring them along. In no time at all, we had dug out the snow from beneath the wheels and placed the sacks, together with a piece of broken fence rail under them. We shovelled away the snow in front of the wheels, until the shovels scraped on concrete. It was then a simple matter of driving slowly forward onto the hard surface. We tossed the shovels and sacks into the back of the car behind Jet and crept away into the night, relieved to have got off so lightly.

A couple of hours later the scene before us could not have been more of a contrast. Freshly changed and fed, we were about to be watered. Seated on either side of a fire that roared halfway up the chimney, we reached for the bottles of Bass and began to fill our glasses. Jet lay stretched out on the hearthrug, trembling and moaning occasionally as he relived adventures in his dreams. We, in our turn, went over the highs and lows of the season we had enjoyed. I had just told Alec how glad I was that we had made contact again and that hopefully we could look forward to a similar arrangement next season. Alec looked across and lowered his glass.

"Hold you hard 'bor," he said, putting on his best Norfolk dialect. "Thet's not oover yet, we've got two Saturdays a'roost shooting for a start."

"Right," I smiled, raising my glass. "You're on. I'll drink to that."